PHILIP POWELL first discovered the excitement of geology and fossils as a teenager growing up in east Cheshire, where the local hills and nearby Derbyshire Peak District provided ample opportunity to pursue his hobby. Geology has remained his principal interest ever since.

After taking a degree in geology at Oriel College, Oxford, he worked for a year in a museum in Lincolnshire before returning to the University Museum of Natural History at Oxford in 1961. There he spent the next forty years as Assistant Curator of the Geological Collections and developed a special interest in Jurassic reptiles.

Although his work over the years took him on geological excursions to places as varied as Brazil, Canada, the United States and Zambia it was the construction of the M40 road extension through Oxfordshire in 1990 that provided some of his most enjoyable work in the field.

He has recently retired from the Museum, and now hopes to have more time to explore Oxfordshire's geology.

FOLLOWING PAGES
Wittenham Clumps, one of the Sinodun Hills,
Malmstone hills with a capping of Lower Chalk.

THE DOVECOTE PRESS

The Geology of
OXFORDSHIRE

PHILIP POWELL

Arngrove Stone with the ammonite *Cardioceras*.

First published in 2005 by
The Dovecote Press Ltd
Stanbridge, Wimborne, Dorset BH21 4JD

ISBN 1 904349 19 6

© Philip Powell 2005

Philip Powell has asserted his rights under the Copyright, Designs
and Patent Act 1988 to be identified as author of this work

Printed and bound in Singapore by KHL Printing Co Ltd

All papers used by The Dovecote Press are natural, recyclable products
made from wood grown in sustainable, well-managed forests.

A CIP catalogue record for this book is available
from the British Library

1 3 5 7 9 8 6 4 2

CONTENTS

INTRODUCTION

The varied landscapes of Oxfordshire have been fashioned by the underlying rocks, by the weather and by the activities of man but the rocks are the basis of all that we see at the surface. Although there is no dramatic scenery in Oxfordshire, no sea cliffs or craggy peaks, the rocks beneath the gentle surface have largely determined the pattern and character of human settlement through water supply, soil type and the provision of building materials. The object of this little book is to explain something of how the rocks were formed and of their arrangement. The story begins 200,000,000 years ago and it should be kept in mind that Oxfordshire as we know it today has been shaped only in the last few thousand years. In this account Oxfordshire can mean either the modern geographical entity or else the site as it was at some remote time.

To a modern Oxonian travelling back in time, the landscape would soon become unfamiliar and would eventually disappear under the sea. Journeying back still farther, the traveller would observe a succession of seascapes, only occasionally giving way to dry land where Oxfordshire ought to be. It is the muds and sands deposited in the seas of those distant times, now transformed into rocks, that build the land we live on. The following chapters present a chronological account of those changes of geography and climate and the rocks they produced.

Chapter One is an outline of the geology of Oxfordshire. Chapter Two briefly describes the ancient rocks that lie buried, like foundations, beneath the rocks that form the modern landscape. Each of the following chapters deals with a main phase of the history and is accompanied by a map of where its rocks appear. Technical terms have been avoided as far as possible but those that are used are printed in bold to direct the reader to the Glossary.

The book is not intended to be used as guide to geological sites. Apart from the old cement quarry at Kirtlington, now laid out with a well explained public geological trail, all the

other sites mentioned are on private land. Quarries, road cuttings, pipeline excavations and other such sites, can be dangerous places because of hazards such as unstable rock faces, deep water and moving machinery. The best way to visit such places to see the rocks and to collect fossils is to join excursions arranged by local geology clubs. Contact names can be obtained at local museums, particularly the Oxford University Museum of Natural History (address on page 103) where there is also a gallery entirely devoted to the geology of Oxfordshire with a display of rock specimens and hundreds of fossils.

PHILIP POWELL

OXFORD, *October 2005*

Shenlow Hill, north-west Oxfordshire. Upper Lias Clay with a cap of Northampton Sand (*see pages 23 and 26*).

ONE

AN OUTLINE OF THE GEOLOGY

The bones of the landscape are the rocks at the surface. They originated as deposits of mud and sand in the seas of the Jurassic and Cretaceous **Periods** between 200 million and 65 million years ago. At the end of the Cretaceous, sea levels

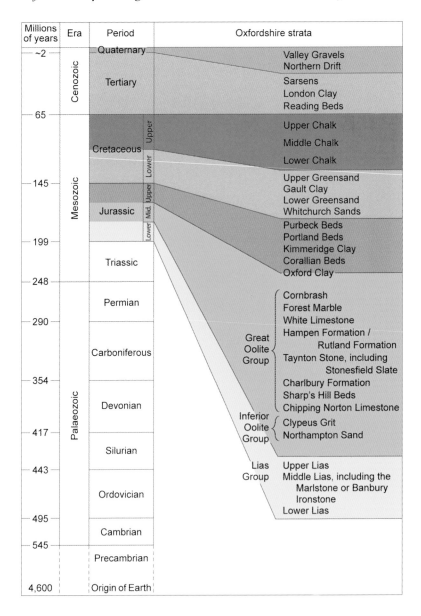

Table of geological periods and Oxfordshire strata.

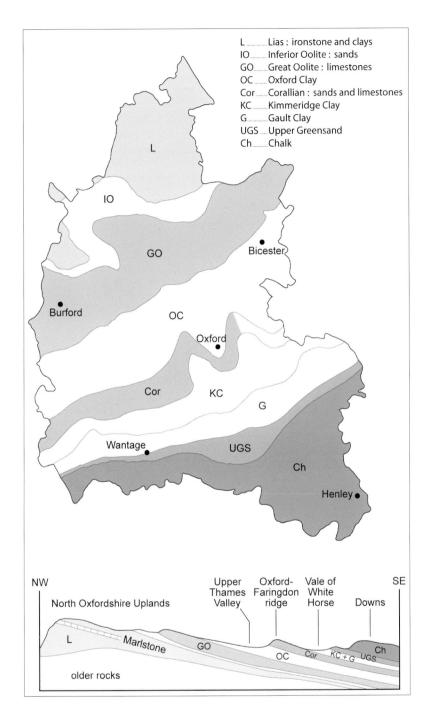

The geological structure of Oxfordshire.

fell and Oxfordshire became dry land.

During the following period, the Tertiary, while erosion was wearing down the newly emerged rocks, earth movements tilted the pile of Jurassic and Cretaceous rocks to the south-east so that they now lie relative to the surface like tiles on a roof. Although the angle of tilt is less than one degree it is sufficient to present the edges of the eroded strata at the

9

ABOVE Near Hornton, in north-west Oxfordshire. The red fields show the connection between geology and landscape. The soil is coloured by iron oxides from the weathering of the underlying Marlstone, a limestone so rich in iron that it was formerly quarried as ore.

OPPOSITE PAGE. A geological map of the Oxford region.
(based on Fig.1 in Geologists' Association Guide no.3: The Oxford District, 1973, by W.S.Mckerrow and W.J.Kennedy.)

surface as bands of rock aligned from south-west to north-east.

The bands of strata broadly comprise alternating groups of clay and limestone. The clays have eroded more deeply, resulting in a landscape of clay vales alternating with limestone scarps and upland. Thus, the limestone uplands of north Oxfordshire slope gently down into the clay vale of the upper Thames. Then follows a ridge of limestones and sands stretching from Oxford to Faringdon. This, in turn, descends southwards into the Vale of White Horse and its continuation east of the Thames as the Vale of Aylesbury. Finally, the sequence finishes with the high Chalk scarps of the Downs and Chilterns. The broad picture is, of course, complicated by faults, by variations in thickness and the lateral extent of individual beds and by dissection and sculpting due to rivers.

The final sculpting of the rocks into the modern landscape took place during the last few hundred thousand years in the Pleistocene **Epoch** when ice sheets more than once reached the northern borders of Oxfordshire and the rivers, greatly swollen by meltwater, carved deep valleys and spread vast quantities of ice-shattered rock as sheets of gravel.

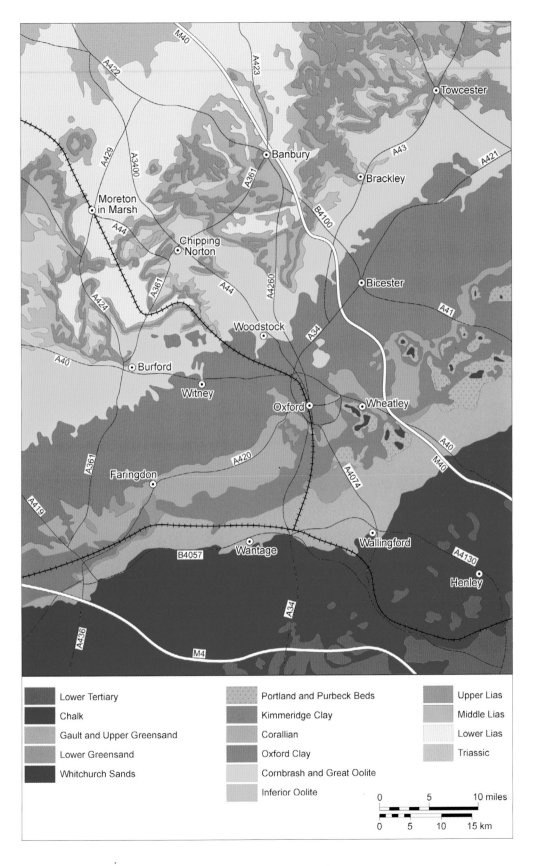

▓ Lower Tertiary	▒ Portland and Purbeck Beds	▓ Upper Lias
▓ Chalk	▓ Kimmeridge Clay	▓ Middle Lias
▓ Gault and Upper Greensand	▓ Corallian	░ Lower Lias
▓ Lower Greensand	▓ Oxford Clay	░ Triassic
▓ Whitchurch Sands	░ Cornbrash and Great Oolite	
	░ Inferior Oolite	

0   5   10 miles

0   5   10   15 km

TWO

THE FOUNDATIONS

The **rocks** at the surface in Oxfordshire – the clays, sands and limestones beneath the soil cover – had their beginnings as sediments deposited in the seas of the Jurassic and Cretaceous Periods between 200 million and 65 million years ago. They were laid down on a surface made up of a variety of pre-existing rocks with long histories of their own. Knowledge of this ancient buried landscape, which rises to nearly 100 metres below modern ground level in the Bicester area, comes from boreholes drilled to explore for oil, gas, coal and for scientific information.

The oldest rocks of this buried surface are known from boreholes just over the county border in Buckinghamshire. They are sandstones and mudstones laid down in the Lower Ordovician Period, some 490 million years ago. Similar rocks are found in Shropshire and Herefordshire and regional geological studies show that they are the remains of the floor of a shallow sea that covered much of what is now the Midlands. This sea lay between the northern edge of a great continent and deeper ocean waters to the north. Late in the Ordovician the Midland area was dry land and no sedimentary strata of this age are present.

Throughout the following period, the Silurian, the central and southern Midlands were again covered by shallow sea while deeper water lay over Wales and East Anglia. Boreholes at Bicester have encountered early Silurian rocks in the form of shallow-water sandstones resting on ashes and lavas from the volcanoes which were active to the west at this time.

Late Silurian to mid Devonian times saw the culmination of powerful earth movements which created a new continent that included parts of modern Russia, Scandinavia, Scotland, Greenland and north-eastern Canada. Oxfordshire and the south Midlands lay on its southern edge as a low-lying, semi-arid plain with ocean to the south. Rivers draining the uplands carried sand and mud to our area, forming floodplains with meandering channels and temporary lakes. Today these sediments are rocks that underlie almost the whole of the county, though separated from the Jurassic cover by those of

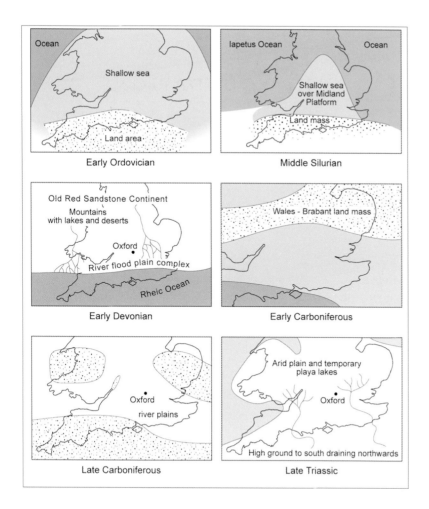

Early Ordovician

Middle Silurian

Early Devonian

Early Carboniferous

Late Carboniferous

Late Triassic

the Carboniferous and Triassic Periods. They have been reached in several boreholes such as the one at Shellingford near Faringdon. There, Devonian red sandstones and siltstones containing fragments of fossil plants were penetrated between 660 metres below ground and the bottom of the hole at over 1000 metres.

In the lower Carboniferous Period shallow sea once again covered most of southern England, while to the south lay deeper ocean water. Muddy, shelly limestones of this age have been found in boreholes at Aston Tirrold near Wallingford and at Foudry Bridge near Reading. Overlying them are sandstones and mudstones of the Upper Carboniferous. By this time the region had risen out of the sea as it was squeezed between slowly approaching continental masses and had become broad river plains supplied by sediment from the surrounding uplands.

The British area by now straddled the equator, having been drifting northwards from the southern hemisphere for many

Maps of generalised geography of southern England before the Jurassic Period.

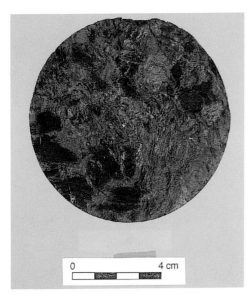

The core section of a coal seam from the Witney borehole.

millions of years (see page 90, on earth movements). The tropical plains supported lush rain forests where dead vegetation accumulated as thick deposits of peat that have since been transformed into coal. The thickest of the coal-bearing sequences in Oxfordshire has been proved in the Apley Barn borehole near Witney. Two groups of coals were recorded, lying between 450 and 875 metres below ground. Of the many coal seams, over twenty are more than 0.46 metres thick and the thickest is 1.5 metres.

By Permian times Britain had become dry land with ranges of hills and an arid climate. Oxfordshire was part of a hot, rocky desert but no rocks of this age are known from here.

By the Triassic, all the earth's continental masses had assembled to form a single supercontinent called Pangaea. Oxfordshire, lying in the interior, was part of an extensive desert region with a hot and generally arid climate. The surrounding uplands comprised the Mendips, Charnwood Forest and the London Platform. Storms and sporadic wet periods brought quantities of red mud down to the Midland plains and to their complex of shallow, brackish lakes. The red sandstones and mudstones that formed from these desert sediments have been encountered in boreholes in the western side of the county, for example at Shellingford near Faringdon, Sarsden near Chipping Norton and Withycombe Farm near Banbury.

By the end of the Triassic, movements in the earth's crust were beginning to cause the breakup of Pangaea. Seaways opened up around Britain and the sea slowly crept across the desert lowlands. Evidence of these shallow marine and lagoonal conditions takes the form of thin mudstones and muddy limestones lying immediately beneath the Jurassic cover right across the county. These rocks have been found in many boreholes, such as at Apley Barn, Shellingford, Sarsden and Withycombe Farm. Finally, the Triassic gave way to the Jurassic as much of southern England became submerged.

The rise in sea level was a world-wide phenomenon related to ocean floor rifting which allowed vast quantities of molten rock to well up from below the crust, building submarine mountains and thereby displacing huge volumes of water. Sea levels continued to rise gradually throughout the Jurassic and Cretaceous Periods but with pauses during which some areas became dry land again. Not until the Upper Cretaceous was north-western Europe largely submerged. During this long period Oxfordshire was situated at the western edge of the

London Platform – a tract of old rocks extending into Belgium – which throughout remained above sea level or only slightly submerged. The shoreline advanced eastwards or retreated westwards according to the fluctuations in sea level. In Oxfordshire this situation resulted in a relatively thin succession of strata with many internal discontinuities due to erosion or to lack of sedimentation, corresponding to shallowing or to emergence as dry land.

THREE

LOWER JURASSIC

The Jurassic Period lasted about 60 million years. During most of that time this area was covered by the sea and lay nearer the equator. At the beginning of the Jurassic Oxfordshire was located between 30 and 35 degrees North, about the latitude of present-day Morocco. By the end of the Jurassic Oxfordshire had drifted another 5 degrees farther north.

The climate was generally warm and humid. The seas supported a wide diversity and abundance of animals such as corals, bivalves, belemnites and ammonites, as well as fishes and large reptiles. Land areas were well clothed with vegetation and inhabited by a variety of dinosaurs and a number of ancient kinds of mammals.

The rock formations of the Jurassic are divided into Lower, Middle and Upper parts on the basis of the clear three-fold grouping of the rocks of this age in the Jura Mountains of eastern France and Switzerland, where they are well represented and from where the Period takes its name. In

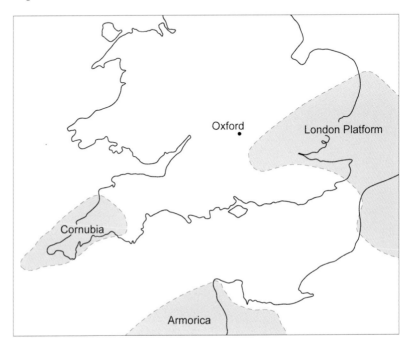

Lower Lias palaeogeography.

Oxfordshire the Lower Jurassic is represented mostly by clays, the Middle Jurassic mostly by limestones and the Upper Jurassic by both clays and limestones.

The Lower Jurassic is often called the Lias, a term derived from an old French word meaning a compact limestone. The Lias itself is divided into Lower, Middle and Upper sections, which correspond to three major environmental episodes. In Lower Lias times most of north-west Europe was covered by sea. Shallowing took place in Middle Lias times and deeper water returned in the Upper Lias.

Outcrop map of Lower Lias rocks.

LOWER LIAS

Rising sea levels at the beginning of the Jurassic progressively drowned most of southern Britain and deposited a blanket of mud which we now see as the clays and muddy limestones of the Lower Lias. These rocks are already familiar to the many people who visit Lyme Regis in Dorset to explore the cliffs and beaches famous for their ichthyosaurs and other fossil treasures.

The outcrop of the Lower Lias extends north-eastwards across England in a belt of low-lying country stretching from Dorset to Yorkshire. In our region the Lower Lias clays form the floor of the Vale of Moreton. Within the county they underlie Banbury and the valleys of the Cherwell, the Sor Brook and the Evenlode and they can be seen where these rivers have cut down through the overlying, younger formations.

In the Cherwell valley, the river runs on Lower Lias clay which reaches as far south as Dane Hill, south of Deddington. Lower Lias clay also forms the low-lying tract of heavy pasture land around Nether Worton to the west of Deddington. In the Evenlode valley it extends as far south as Dean Grove, near Charlbury.

The clay is generally seen only in temporary exposures such as excavations for foundations or road works. The nearest permanent exposure is near Blockley, in Gloucestershire, 5 kilometres north-west of Moreton-in-Marsh, where the clay is dug for brickmaking.

The section in the pit at Blockley exposes 14 metres of blue-grey clay in which the well-preserved ammonite *Liparoceras* is common. About a third of the way down is a band, less than half a metre thick, of brown calcareous mudstone packed with

An ammonite, *Liparoceras*, from the Lower Lias clay of Blockley near Moreton-in-Marsh.

Lower Lias Fossils.

RIGHT The ammonite *Androgynoceras lataecostata* and the bivalve *Oxytoma inequivalvis*; Warkworth, near Banbury.

BELOW (clockwise from top left) *Protocardia truncata*; Kings Sutton. *Amberleya subimbricata, Modiolus scalprum* (a mussel), *Isocrinus robustus* (part of the stem of a sea lily or crinoid); M40 road cutting, Warmington, north-west of Banbury.

a range of bivalves and other invertebrate fossils. Two or three partial skeletons of plesiosaurs have also been found in the pit. These extinct marine reptiles are typically two or three metres long, and shaped like a shell-less turtle with a long neck. The presence of ammonites and plesiosaurs indicates that the clays were laid down in open sea conditions. Other lines of evidence suggest that the water was a few tens of metres deep.

The Lower Lias clay has in the past been dug for brickmaking at places all over the outcrop, for example Gibbs Quarry to the south of Deddington and in various pits around Banbury. In the quarry just north of Banbury station, a bed of hard, shelly limestone around 30 cm thick occurred. Named Banbury Marble it was extracted and used locally for ornamental work such as fireplaces.

At the time the clay at Blockley was being deposited the Lower Lias sea had reached its maximum extent. It had encroached on the London Platform but not submerged it.

Banbury Marble, a band of hard limestone in the Lower Lias around Banbury. The cross sections of bivalve shells preserved in white calcite contrast with the dark, organic-rich matrix. In the 19th century this stone was polished and used for ornamental purposes in the town.

Information from boreholes shows how this upstanding area affected sedimentation during the general rise in sea level through Lower Lias time. The parts of the basin farthest from the London Platform had been under water for longer and had thus accumulated more sediment. In the borehole at Stowell Park, near Northleach, the Lower Lias is more than 360 metres thick. Farther east, at Apley Barn, near Witney, it is nearly 120 metres. Still farther east, at Chalgrove, the Lower Lias is represented by only 7 metres of clay.

Lower Lias times gradually came to an end as sea levels began to fall. This change is recorded in the rock sequence as a gradual increase in silt over clay, leading up to the sands and silts of the Middle Lias. Silt and sand imply a nearer proximity to the source of sediment – the land – since coarser, heavier particles are dropped when water currents no longer have the power to move them. Only the smallest particles are carried far out to sea.

Blockley Quarry, near Moreton-in-Marsh. The Lower Lias Clay is dug here for brickmaking.

Outcrop map of Middle Lias rocks.

The Middle Lias is made up of two distinct groups of rocks. The lower part comprises silts and sands, while the upper part is a hard, iron-rich limestone known as the Marlstone Rock Bed, or Banbury Ironstone.

The silts and sands are not often exposed, but they give rise to light, grey-brown, loamy soils which are often evident by a scatter of gorse and broom. In many river valleys of north-west Oxfordshire they form the steep slope of the valley side below the prominent feature of the Marlstone Rock Bed. Where they meet the flat floor of Lower Lias clay, the junction may be marked by springs.

The sands and silts are pale buff or blue, usually with abundant little flakes of silvery mica. Ferruginous nodules and beds of ferruginous silt occur in places. Locally the sands are cemented into masses of hard rock which often preserve plentiful fossils. The rich and diverse fauna includes bivalves, gastropods, belemnites, ammonites and brachiopods.

The Marlstone Rock Bed, which makes up the upper part of the Middle Lias, is a hard, iron-rich limestone which usually has a rich red-brown colour, but can appear green or bluish green where it is unweathered. It occurs widely across north Oxfordshire and on the east side of the Cherwell, often forming a bench on the sides of the valleys. It forms extensive plateaux between Hook Norton, Bodicote and Deddington. Most notably it gives rise to the plateau country north-west of Banbury, culminating in the great escarpment which, at Edge

The Middle Lias; M40 road construction, Aynho. The blue sands, including the hard band at the base are Lower Middle Lias. The overlying brown rock is upper Middle Lias or Marlstone.

Hill, stands over 100 metres above the Lower Lias clays in the vale below. The plateau is deeply incised down to Lower Lias clays by the valleys of the south-easterly draining Sor Brook and its tributaries. On the north-eastern side of the plateau another stream has cut a similar valley that separates off the Burton Dassett hills, a range 12 kilometres long capped by Marlstone. On their eastern side the hills are separated from the main outcrop of the Marlstone in Northamptonshire by the valley of the River Cherwell.

The Marlstone has been exploited, under a number of different names for a variety of uses. As a building stone, it is generally called Hornton stone, after the village near Edge Hill where it was dug. For centuries this stone has been used for local buildings ranging from manor houses and churches to cottages and pigsties, and for gateposts, troughs and flagstones. Slabs made into gravestones are common in churchyards over a very wide area of Oxfordshire. Quarries at Hornton and Great Tew are still producing building stone. Its

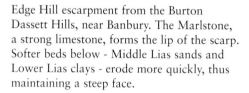

Edge Hill escarpment from the Burton Dassett Hills, near Banbury. The Marlstone, a strong limestone, forms the lip of the scarp. Softer beds below - Middle Lias sands and Lower Lias clays - erode more quickly, thus maintaining a steep face.

The Marlstone at Great Tew being dug for building stone. The overlying blue clay is Upper Lias.

A Marlstone building at Hornton, near Banbury.

Brachiopods of the Marlstone.
TOP *Tetrarhynchia tetraedra* and BOTTOM
Lobothyris punctata; Banbury area.

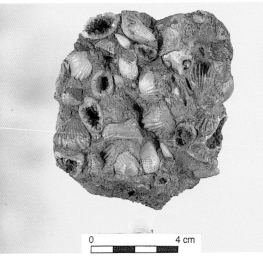

0   4 cm

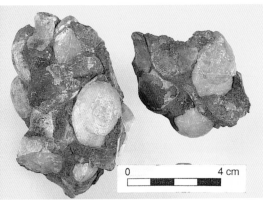

0   4 cm

rich, warm, gingerbread colour lends a special individuality and beauty to this upland corner of Oxfordshire.

Under the name Banbury Ironstone, the Marlstone Rock Bed has also served as a source of iron ore. Exploitation began in the late 1850s and carried on for just over 100 years. Pits were opened first at Fawler, near Charlbury, and later at Adderbury, Steeple Aston and other sites in the Cherwell Valley. These other sites were chosen, no doubt, because their proximity to the railway meant the ore could be economically transported to smelters in other parts of the country. The Banbury Ironstone is thickest in the area extending from Edge Hill south-east through Hornton, Alkerton and Wroxton to Bloxham. It was opened up as a source of iron ore around 1920, thanks to the construction of a mineral railway. By the middle of the 20th century, the opencast pits around Wroxton had working faces nearly 3 kilometres long and up to 10 metres high. When each pit had been worked out the overburden and soil were replaced and the land returned to farming. These fields were now 5 to 10 metres below their original level and the roads alongside the pits are left perched on strips of unquarried Marlstone. The last pit in production was at Wroxton but by the end of 1967 it too had closed.

The characteristic colour of the Marlstone is the rich reddish brown seen in buildings in Ironstone villages such as Adderbury or Hornton, but the unweathered rock is often green or bluish green. This is due to a mineral called berthierine, a compound mainly of iron and silica and one of the principal components of the original rock. Berthierine is affected by the oxygen dissolved in ground water, which, in effect, causes rusting. The iron in its green, ferrous form is oxidised to a mixture of red, ferric oxides called limonite. An example of the incomplete process can occasionally be seen in a building where the colour passes from green to red in a single block of stone.

The environmental conditions that brought about the formation of ironstone are not well understood. No comparable deposit is forming in the world today. The sea was evidently rather shallow since the rock preserves signs of wave action in the form of ripples, **cross-bedding** and fragments of shells. The bottom supported a fauna dominated by bivalves and colonies of brachiopods. The brachiopods are commonly found preserved in white calcite, in clumps or pockets, still in the places where they lived. Belemnites occur abundantly in a pebbly bed at the base of the Marlstone but are not very common otherwise. Ammonites are rare.

The beginning of the Upper Lias relates to rising sea levels across the region. Deposition of mud replaced the formation of ironstone so that the beds of this age in Oxfordshire are predominantly clays. The clay sequence is about 30 metres thick around Banbury but thins southwards so that at Fawler only 2 to 4 metres are present. In Gloucestershire equivalent deposits are around 90 metres thick and in Northamptonshire around 60 metres. These differences are due partly to the continuing influence of the London Platform and partly to loss of higher beds by erosion when sea level fell again at the end of the Upper Lias.

Around Banbury and to the east and north-east in Northamptonshire the basal bed of the Upper Lias is frequently a friable, buff or brown, ferruginous limestone up to 20 centimetres thick. It lies on top of the Marlstone and grades down into it. It represents the remains of the Marlstone reworked by the deepening Upper Lias sea. Although intimately connected to the Marlstone it is replete with fossils of Upper Lias age and has therefore been called the Transition Bed. The ammonites *Tiltoniceras acutum* and species of *Dactylioceras* are abundant but the fauna includes many other beautifully preserved fossils, especially gastropods, bivalves and brachiopods.

Elsewhere, near the base of the clay, there are usually two or three bands of pale, muddy limestone, each about 20 centimetres thick. They are generally packed with fossils, mostly ammonites, especially species of *Harpoceras*, *Hildoceras* and *Dactylioceras*. These beds are seldom exposed but where they lie near the surface a scattering of fossiliferous brash on the ground above indicates their presence.

In the north a few isolated remnants of the Upper Lias beds lie on the ironstone plateau between Banbury and Edge Hill. The main outcrop lies within the area bounded by Sutton-under-Brailes, Compton Wynyates, Shenlow Hill, Shutford, Bloxham, Milcombe and Hook Norton. Farther south a detached broad strip stretches from Little Tew via Great Tew to Duns Tew. To the west the Upper Lias forms part of the scarp overlooking Long Compton and Little Compton in the Vale of Moreton. In the Chipping Norton valley the outcrop on the west side is around a kilometre wide between Great Rollright and Salford. East of Chipping Norton the Upper Lias

Outcrop map of Upper Lias rocks.

Transition Bed fossils.
TOP The ammonite *Tiltoniceras acutum* and BOTTOM scallops *Pseudopecten (left)* and *Camptonectes*; Aynho, south-east of Banbury.

Yarn Hill, near Epwell; formed of Upper Lias clay capped with Northampton Sand.

occurs between Heythrop and Enstone where the River Glyme has cut a window through the overlying, younger rocks. Similarly it forms the floor of the Dorn valley around and southeast of Middle Barton. Eastwards again, in the Cherwell valley, it stretches down to Northbrook, a little north of Tackley. On the east side the outcrop gradually widens northwards into Northamptonshire. The southernmost appearance is at Fawler in the Evenlode valley.

The Upper Lias clays were formerly widely exploited for brickmaking. Works sprang up across the region in the nineteenth century as increasing population and rising standards in housing, drainage and so on lead to a greater demand for bricks. Pits opened at Gallow Hill near Lower Brailes, Constitution Hill in Banbury, Bloxham, Little Tew, Fawler and a number of other sites.

Upper Lias ammonites.
TOP *Harpoceras*.
CENTRE *Hildoceras*.
BOTTOM *Dactylioceras*.
Aynho, south-east of Banbury.

FOUR

MIDDLE JURASSIC

Towards the end of Upper Lias times sea levels fell somewhat, bringing a change of conditions which initiated the Middle Jurassic. Relatively low sea levels persisted for about 15 million years and in the clear, warm, shallow waters the most important sediment was calcium carbonate. The accumulations of carbonate mud and carbonate sand have been transformed into a variety of limestones which are grouped into two series called the Inferior Oolite and the Great Oolite.

The word oolite refers to a rock containing a proportion of ooliths. These are little spheres of calcium carbonate, typically half to one millimetre in diameter. The name comes from the Greek word *oon* – meaning egg – because a densely oolitic limestone has the appearance of fish roe.

The Inferior Oolite group of formations is so called not because of any inferior quality but because its rocks are older than, and therefore stratigraphically below, those of the Great Oolite. In fact it supplies many excellent building stones. In the Cotswolds, for example, there is the yellow Guiting Stone of the Chipping Campden district. In Northamptonshire,

Oolitic limestone; from near Witney. This rock is composed almost entirely of tiny spheres of calcium carbonate called ooliths. This term comes from the Greek word oon, meaning an egg, because oolitic rock resembles fish roe.

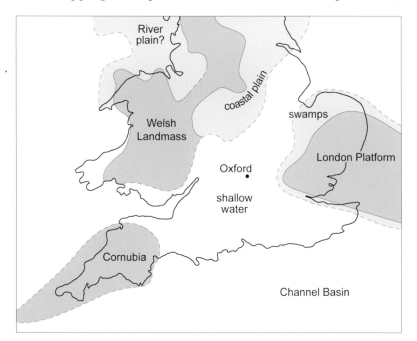

Middle Jurassic palaeogeography.

Outcrop map of the Inferior Oolite.

Inferior Oolite ammonites. LEFT *Leioceras*, Hook Norton; RIGHT *Ludwigia*, near Cheltenham (the red and white paint has been applied to make certain structures clear).

Rutland and Lincolnshire there are famous stones such as Ketton, Ancaster and Weldon, as well as Clipsham, much used for restoring the historic buildings of Oxford.

During Inferior Oolite and Great Oolite times Oxfordshire was a low-lying area between shallow sea to the south-west and a swampy, coastal region to the north-east. In these shallow, variable environments the deposition of sediment varied greatly in amount and type from place to place and from time to time. As a result the strata exhibit rapid lateral changes in thickness and character and some beds may be restricted to relatively small areas.

The Inferior Oolite is well represented by limestones in the Cotswolds and in Lincolnshire and by ferruginous sands, muds and thin limestones in Northamptonshire. In Oxfordshire, however, beds equivalent only to the earliest and latest of those in the Cotswold sequence are found. During most of Inferior Oolite time the area was part of the London Platform and was dry land or extremely shallow sea so that no sediments were deposited to represent this period as rocks.

The Lower Inferior Oolite beds to the south and west of Chipping Norton are sandy limestones similar to those of the north Cotswolds. North and north-east of Chipping Norton the beds become progressively more sandy and ferruginous and grade into their lateral equivalent, the Northampton Sand Formation. The limestones which are thin and patchy have been recorded in the past in a number of small quarries, including Oatley Hill near Hook Norton, the railway cutting at Hook Norton, Milcombe, near Bloxham and at Coombe Hill and Blackingrove near Deddington. Among the collections of fossils from these places are ammonites that confirm the Inferior Oolite age, including species of *Ludwigia*, and *Leioceras*.

North-west of Hook Norton brown sands and sandy limestones form the tops of Brailes Hill, Mine Hill and Round Hill. Similar rocks form an extensive outcrop around Ryehill Farm right on the county border and around Sibford Gower and Sibford Ferris to the east. The Northampton Sand makes the bulk of the high ground around Wigginton Heath, including Council Hill and Rye Hill, and forms the outliers to the east, Fern Hill and Hobb Hill. Further patches occur around Tadmarton and Tadmarton Lodge. North-west of Tadmarton the sands cap the Upper Lias on a string of small, steep-sided, conspicuous hills: Madmarston Hill, Jesters Hill, Barton Hill, Long Hill, Yarn Hill, Epwell Hill and Shenlow Hill.

In the Cherwell Valley the formation comprises friable, brown, sandy and shelly limestones or calcareous sands which extend as far down as Northbrook, 2 or 3 kilometres north of Kirtlington. At Steeple Aston, this ferruginous rock was once dug for iron ore, along with the Marlstone from deeper down, by means of a 30-metre deep shaft

Both ironstones have been used for buildings in the village. The Northampton Sand is redder and is sandy while the Marlstone is browner and often fossiliferous with belemnites and brachiopods. A short distance north-west of Steeple Aston, the Northampton Sand can be seen in the lower part of the quarry near Horsehay Farm, Duns Tew. There it appears as 2-3 metres of brown sand with some friable shelly limestone.

During the next eight million years or so, while limestones continued to accumulate in the Cotswold area, Oxfordshire remained dry land or extremely shallow sea.

Towards the end of Inferior Oolite times the scene changed again when a rise in sea level rise connected Oxfordshire with the Cotswold basin. The deposits of this sea are now a limestone called the Clypeus Grit. It is not a true grit because it does not contain angular grains of quartz. The first part of the name refers to the sea urchin, *Clypeus ploti*, which it does include in great abundance. The Clypeus Grit forms the floor of the Town Quarry at Charlbury. Boreholes around the area prove the formation to be about 7.5 metres thick. Northwards it thins away so that at Hook Norton Railway cutting it appears as only half a metre of hard limestone with fossil corals. Eastwards it thins and dies out between Charlbury and the Cherwell Valley. Southwards it passes under younger rocks.

The usual character of the Clypeus Grit over most of its extent is a pale buff, coarse-grained limestone with a pasty groundmass mixed with fragments of shells and abundant medium to large ooliths. It weathers to rubble and is no use as a building stone, apart from one remarkable development in Wychwood Forest. At Cornbury Park, across the Evenlode from Charlbury, a deep quarry produced a high quality stone used to build the 17th century mansion. In the next century, the same quarry was worked again for the building of Blenheim Palace. There the stone has weathered to a golden yellow colour and fragments and whole shells of *Clypeus* can be clearly seen.

Oxfordshire was now fully connected to the Cotswold basin and to the open sea that covered most of southern England. The London Platform was still dry land and its western shore

Horsehay Quarry, Duns Tew. The section shows about 2 metres of brown Northampton Sand at the base. Above are paler sands of the Horsehay Sand Formation, a lateral equivalent of the Chipping Norton Limestone Formation. Above the white sand are the clays and patchy limestones of the Sharp's Hill Formation.

Clypeus ploti, a fossil sea urchin from Burford. Robert Plot in his book, *The Natural History of Oxfordshire*, 1677, notes that, "...all about Burford they are found in such plenty that I believe it were easy, in a little time to procure a cartload..."

Outcrop map of the Great Oolite.

Taynton Stone. Ooliths are represented by little cavities, having been plucked out by the saw blade. What remains is the calcite cement that surrounded them, and the denser bands composed of shell fragments. These bands are more resistant to weathering and often stand out as ribs in old stones such as parapets and gargoyles.

The banding results from the action of the currents that deposited the original sediment. Mud particles were swept away, leaving only ooliths and shell fragments. As the current slackened, pieces of shell settled out first, then larger ooliths, then progressively smaller ooliths. Then another pulse deposited the next shell layer, and so on.

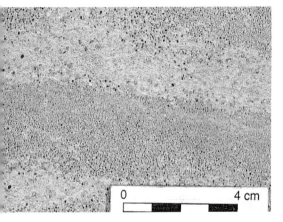

was more or less the line of the present Cherwell Valley.

GREAT OOLITE

For the next 5 million years sediments which we now recognise as the Great Oolite Group of rock formations accumulated in Oxfordshire. Limestones appear to predominate, but there is also much clay and sand and the character and thickness of all the beds varies from place to place. This variation results from factors connected with Oxfordshire's near-shore situation. Minor fluctuations of sea level altered the relative position of the coastline and depositional environments shifted accordingly. Three main environments, representing different zones of the gently sloping sea bed, each produced its characteristic rock type.

In the open sea to the south-west, active water circulation by storms and waves winnowed the sediments, removing the mud particles so that lime sands accumulated. These consisted mainly of ooliths and shell fragments. The Taynton Stone is a typical product.

Closer to the shore, storm and wave action was baffled by the outer shoals and calm, marine lagoons developed. In the quiet water green algae flourished. These organisms secrete calcium carbonate and when they die and decay large quantities of tiny needles of the carbonate are released, producing lime mud. This is what gives rise to the fine grained, pasty-looking limestones that make up, for example, many of the beds in the White Limestone. Typical examples are easily accessible in the Geological Trail at the old Kirtlington cement quarry.

Even closer to the shore the lagoons formed a barrier to the seaward movement of silt and clay carried by rivers draining the London Platform. This sediment formed mudbanks and swamps. Evidence of swamp vegetation is preserved as rootlet beds. The rocks that formed under these varied and variable environmental conditions present differences of character and thickness from place to place. Correlation, that is demonstrating the contemporaneity of rocks in different locations, is therefore difficult, especially as ammonites are so rare because they are creatures of the open sea

The Great Oolite Group of rocks forms the upland limestone belt that stretches across north Oxfordshire from Burford in the south-west to Buckingham in the north-east, attaining its greatest width between Woodstock and Chipping

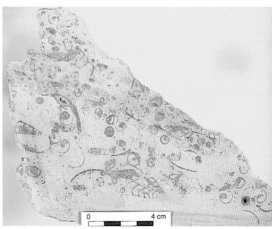

Norton. North-westwards it forms the southern boundary of the Marlstone plateau. To the south-east it dips below the Oxford Clay. This mass of rocks is divided into units called formations, each named after a characteristic lithology or place where it is typically developed

The first, or oldest of these formations is the Chipping Norton Limestone Formation. It is typically a fawn, sandy limestone, but it varies in the normal Great Oolite way, reflecting the Jurassic geography. As a result, it passes into clay (Fuller's Earth) south-westwards where there was deeper water, and into sands towards the north-east nearer the shore line. These sands were formerly dug as building material in pits around Great Tew and Swerford. In the Cherwell valley they can be seen at the Horsehay Farm Pit, where they overlie the Northampton Sand and where they appear as about twelve metres of pale sands with bands of lilac-coloured silt and clay

ABOVE White Limestone; Worsham, near Witney. The ground-mass of fine-grained calcium carbonate is the lime mud deposited in the calm, shallow waters close to the shore. The fossils are gastropods, *Aphanoptyxis excavata*, and fragments of bivalve shells.

ABOVE LEFT A rootlet bed; M40 road cutting, Fritwell, south-east of Banbury. These traces of ancient roots in sandy rock represent marshes along the coast in Great Oolite times.

Town Quarry, Charlbury, in 1989. The lowest beds are sandy limestones of the Chipping Norton Limestone Formation. The dark band above is the clays of the Sharp's Hill Formation. Above are the buff-coloured limestones of the Charlbury Formation which are succeeded by the paler Taynton Limestone Formation.

TOP William Smith (1769 -1839) aged 69. His pioneering work on the order of arrangement of stratified rocks and the use of fossils to identify them earned for him the title, 'The Father of English Geology'.

ABOVE The William Smith monument at Churchill, near Chipping Norton. The inscription reads, 'In memory of William Smith 'The Father of British Geology' born at Churchill March 23 1769 died at Northampton August 28 1839.'

OPPOSITE PAGE William Smith's Geological Map of Oxfordshire, 1820.

and abundant fossil plant debris throughout.

Near Chipping Norton itself, the limestone is a white oolitic **freestone** from which the town was largely built. Chipping Norton limestone was also used for most of the buildings in Charlbury and in many other villages in the area. Good stone came from quarries such as the group of old pits around Lyneham Barrow, 6 km south of Chipping Norton, and from the Town Quarry, Charlbury, which has only recently closed.

A tough **siliceous** form of the Chipping Norton Limestone was used by the local people 4,000 years or so ago to make the stone circle of the Rollright Stones. Blocks of the same material line the village street at Churchill and a slab 2 metres or so long as been raised to make the monument to the village's most famous son, William Smith, 'the Father of British Geology' as the plaque records.

Smith was born in 1769, son of a blacksmith. Although he received only a rudimentary formal education, he was a keen observer and eager to learn. He became a land surveyor and went to work in Somerset. In the course of his work in the coal mines and in the construction of a coal-carrying canal, Smith noticed that the layers of rock that he encountered could be individually identified by the assemblage of fossils that each one contained. Further, he noticed that the layers or beds always occurred in the same order wherever they were found, so that in a sequence of beds of rocks which have been formed by the deposition of sediment, a particular layer is older than the one above it and younger than the one below it. The application of these two ideas enabled beds to be correlated across large distances

These ideas are the basis of stratigraphy and their dissemination gave a huge impetus to the developing science of geology. Smith's knowledge of stratigraphy gave him a three dimensional understanding of strata which he could represent as a map. His map of the strata around Bath, dated 1799, is the oldest geological map in the world. By 1815 he had published the first geological map of the whole of England and Wales. Smith received due recognition for his ideas and achievements only in 1831 when the prestigious Geological Society of London conferred on him their highest honour, the Wollaston Medal. The President, in his address, called William Smith "the Father of English Geology".

Overlying the Chipping Norton Limestone Formation in north Oxfordshire is the Sharp's Hill Formation, named after the quarry (now overgrown) at Sharp's Hill near Hook

A
NEW MAP
OF
OXFORDSHIRE,
DIVIDED INTO HUNDREDS.
EXHIBITING
Its Roads, Rivers, Parks, &c.
By JOHN CARY, Engraver.
1820.

SCALE

The Thames in flood at Radcot Bridge, north of Faringdon. The bridge was built of Taynton Stone in the late 12th century. From nearby wharves Taynton Stone was transported down the Thames.

Norton. It includes greenish mudstones, thin fossiliferous limestones, silts and clays. Rootlet beds and plant debris are common and the sequence was evidently deposited in lagoons close to the shore. At Sharp's Hill the beds have yielded a few bones of a stegosaur. The bones are not those of *Stegosaurus* itself – the well known dinosaur with two rows of vertical plates along its back – but they are important because they represent one of the earliest appearances of this group of dinosaurs in the geological record.

The Sharp's Hill Beds can still be seen in the remains of the Town Quarry at Charlbury as one to two metres of thin limestones and dark clays with many oyster shells. They are also displayed at Horsehay Quarry, Dun's Tew, near the top of the section as four beds of alternating greenish, shelly clays and fawn, speckled limestones, five to six metres thick.

Above the clays of the Sharp's Hill beds at the Town Quarry are 5 metres or so of buff-coloured limestones, including sandy, oolitic and shelly varieties. These are the Charlbury Formation. It extends about 10 kilometres north-east of Chipping Norton, about 15 kilometres east of Charlbury and dies out west of the county boundary.

The return to more open sea conditions signified by the limestones of the Charlbury Formation is more pronounced in the next rock unit, the Taynton Limestone Formation, or, more informally, the Taynton Stone. This is characterised by coarse-grained, shelly, oolitic limestones, although other varieties occur, including thin-bedded sandy tilestones such as the Fulwell Slate near Enstone, and the famous Stonesfield Slate. The formation extends from the Cotswolds across Oxfordshire and into Northamptonshire in a belt whose edges pass through Churchill in the north and Burford in the south. The northern

A Stonesfield Slate roof at Stonesfield.

edge forms an irregular small scarp, much broken by erosion and faulting. On the ground the Taynton Stone seems to merge with the main mass of Great Oolite limestones which form the southern part of the limestone belt of Oxfordshire.

Around Burford the formation provides good building stones. One of the best of them comes from Taynton, after which the formation is named. The quarries, about three kilometres north-west of Burford, have been worked for centuries. The stone is a coarse-grained freestone consisting of ooliths and pieces of broken shells. Its strength and durability derive from the dense cement of crystalline calcite that fills the spaces between the grains. The stone usually has a markedly stripey appearance. This is due to the grading of the ooliths and shell fragments into different layers according to the strength and direction of the sea currents prevailing at the time of deposition.

The busiest period at the Taynton quarries was from the thirteenth to the sixteenth centuries when large quantities of stone were extracted for building at Windsor Castle, at several Oxford Colleges and for many churches in the region. The durability of the stone is attested by its excellent condition in the Norman work in the tower of Burford Church. Within the Taynton Stone Formation at Stonesfield lens-shaped bodies of calcareous sandstone occur at three different levels. This stone was the source of the **Stonesfield Slate** that from the 17th century to early 20th century provided the tiles that so beautifully complement the stone walls of the vernacular buildings in the district. Tilestones of the same type also occur in the underlying Charlbury and Sharp's Hill Formations and in the overlying Hampen Formation. Other Great Oolite Formations have yielded tilestones from thinly bedded

Part of a Stonesfield Slate tile with characteristic sprinkling of white ooliths and the bivalve *Trigonia impressa*.

A Stonesfield Slate mine; Spratts Barn, Stonesfield. The productive beds are on the left. Waste stone is stacked up on the right to support the roof. This mine was abandoned about 1910.

BELOW Part of the right, lower jaw of *Megalosaurus*, from Stonesfield. This bone, with some others, was the subject of the first scientific account of a dinosaur, by Dr. Buckland in 1824.

The different sizes of the teeth reflect the fact that dinosaurs, like other reptiles, constantly replace them. Some of the longer, mature teeth were broken off before the bone was buried and fossilised. A growing replacement tooth can be seen at the base of the large sixth tooth. The teeth are flattenened from side to side and the edges bear small serrations like those on a modern steak knife.

The bone is on display at the Oxford University Museum of Natural History.

BELOW RIGHT Restoration of *Megalosaurus* by Gareth Monger. The living animal was about 8 metres in length.

limestones or sandy limestones but the best quality Stonesfield slates are thinner and flatter and therefore easier to lay and make a lighter roof.

Stonesfield slates first came into production in the seventeenth century when it was discovered that exposing the freshly dug stone to frost enabled it to be split thinly. The seams of stone, less than two metres thick at the most, were reached by adits driven into the valley sides or by vertical shafts, some of which are still accessible. Mined stone was kept damp until it could be frosted, after which the slate-makers split it and shaped it into the various sizes of tiles. The slate-makers, finding fossils as they worked the blocks, would put them aside for sale to visiting collectors. The fauna of the Stonesfield Slate is therefore well known. It includes not only marine animals such as corals, gastropods, bivalves, belemnites, ammonites, oysters, sharks, bony fishes, turtles and crocodiles, but also elements washed in from nearby land such as dragonflies, eggs, pterosaurs, dinosaurs, mammals, seeds, leaves of conifers and cycads.

The range of vertebrates is unusually extensive and provides an important window into the history of these animals in the Middle Jurassic. The mammals are especially interesting because of their rarity generally in the Jurassic. Although other sites have now produced many more remains of fossil mammals, the eight or nine little jaws from Stonesfield provided, for almost two centuries, the most important information on the early ancestors of modern mammals. These little, shrew-like creatures lived alongside the eight metre long, carnivorous dinosaur, *Megalosaurus*. The big bones of this animal, although far from representing a complete skeleton are nevertheless of great interest and importance because in 1824, the Oxford geologist, the Rev. Dr. William Buckland, made them the subject of the very first scientific description of a dinosaur. They are still on display at the Oxford University

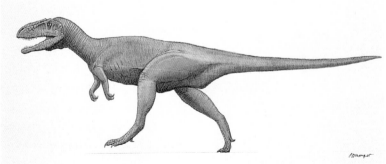

Museum of Natural History.

The Taynton Limestone Formation grades upwards into the Hampen Formation, sometimes still informally called the Hampen Marly Beds in reference to the general marly and clayey character of the formation across much of Oxfordshire. Many beds are very fossiliferous, especially in brachiopods and bivalves, and some beds are packed with vast numbers of small oysters. This indicates a change to shallower, quieter waters. However as the formation is traced north-eastwards more and more beds of non-marine origin are seen to interfinger with the marls and limestones. Beyond Oxford the change of character is more or less complete and the beds belong more with the Rutland Formation of the east Midlands. A typical sequence in the Oxford to Bicester area was displayed in the quarry at Woodeaton. The section comprises about four metres of green, blue, brown, black and grey silts and silty clays containing brackish-water bivalves and land-derived material, including bones of dinosaurs; a **sauropod** and a stegosaur. There are also twigs and leaves representing the forests of the nearby London Platform and some beds are full of the roots of swamp plants. The **White Limestone Formation** which succeeds the Hampen Formation stretches across Oxfordshire from Burford to Bicester and extends into

Fossils of the Stonesfield Slate.
TOP LEFT Dragonfly wing; *Libellula westwoodi* (4.8cm long).
TOP RIGHT An egg, perhaps of a turtle or crocodile and a conifer frond; *Brachyphyllum expansum*.
ABOVE LEFT Mammal jaw; *Phascolotherium bucklandi* (3.3cm long).
ABOVE Part of the jaw of a small crocodile, *Teleosaurus cadomensis*.

BELOW Woodeaton Quarry, north-east of Oxford. Rutland Formation (blue) overlain by the White Limestone.

The White Limestone Formation at Fishers Gate Quarry, North Leigh, near Witney (now filled in).

Restoration of *Cetiosaurus* by Gareth Monger. The living animal was about 15 metres in length.

Buckinghamshire. It forms much of the surface of the plateau, especially around Wootton, Glympton and Kiddington west of the Cherwell and between Bletchingdon and Fritwell east of the Cherwell.

As the name suggests, the formation is predominantly limestone though there are thin clays at many levels, especially in the lower part. The characteristic type of limestone is a cream or buff rock with an exceedingly fine-grained groundmass containing a scattering of ooliths, oolith-like pellets and fragments of shells. In quarries, although the beds appear in regular courses like masonry, within the beds the original lamination has been destroyed by stirring and mixing as bivalves, gastropods, echinoids, crustaceans, and other creatures burrowed through the mud for food or shelter.

This implies a calm marine environment with little tidal influence. Here and there occurred small patch reefs of corals and shell banks of brachiopods. Small changes of sea level occasionally exposed the near-shore mud banks at the surface. At Ardley, for example, the surface of a marine limestone is impressed with hundreds of footprints of dinosaurs that walked across it while it was still soft.

These trackways are of two kinds. First, those with three-toed bird-like footprints of a bipedal, carnivorous **theropod** dinosaur. The prints are up to 80 centimetres long and 2 metres apart. Second, there are pothole-like impressions 60 centimetres across, of the feet of huge, quadrupedal, herbivorous, **sauropod** dinosaurs. No bones have been found to identify the track-makers but the size of the three-toed prints suggests *Megalosaurus*, the only known theropod in the area of appropriate size and geological age. Similarly, the sauropod trackways are likely to have been made by the 15 metres long *Cetiosaurus*, whose bones are found in the White Limestone at several localities in the district, notably at

Kirtlington and Enslow Bridge.

The remains of numerous quarries all over the outcrop testify to the former importance of the formation as a source of lime. In the Cherwell Valley, where the formation reaches its greatest thickness of nearly 20 metres, the proportion of clay to limestone was suitable for cement manufacture. At the Shipton-on-Cherwell cement works quarry, recently closed, the White Limestone was magnificently exposed in faces two and a half kilometres long. At Kirtlington, the old canalside cement quarry now contains a well laid out and informative geological trail open to the public.

At the end of the White Limestone times there was a short period of erosion before the re-establishment of marine conditions and the deposition of the Forest Marble. This formation, named by William Smith after Wychwood Forest, comprises a variable sequence of flaggy limestones, oolitic freestones, sandy limestones and clays. The beds are often deposited in channels cut into the underlying sediments.

The limestones characteristically show pronounced cross-bedding and contain much broken up shell material, especially of oysters. The sandy and muddy beds may have rippled surfaces and plant remains are common in them. These features indicate that the swamps and mudflats of White Limestone times had been replaced by a shallow but open sea, periodically swept by currents, while nearby land supplied sand, mud and plant debris. The 'marble' comes from the coarse-grained, oolitic limestones with abundant dark blue or blue-black fragments of oyster shells, and a cement of crystalline calcite. In the 17th century it was dug at Bletchingdon to make chimney pieces and paving for Bletchingdon House and for Cornbury Park. The best known example of its decorative use is the seven foot high monolithic columns of the porticos of Canterbury Quad at St John's College, Oxford.

Similar stone that occurred in thinner beds was worked in many quarries for walling or for flags for interior paving. The thinnest beds of all, both of shelly limestone and of calcareous sandstone, were widely used in Oxfordshire and Gloucestershire as roof tiles. The Filkins area exemplifies the variability of the Forest Marble; only three kilometres to the north the thin limestones are wholly replaced by clay that is thick enough to have once supported a brickyard.

Lying above the Forest Marble, the topmost formation of the Great Oolite is the Cornbrash, named by William Smith

Dinosaur footprints at Ardley Quarry, near Bicester.
TOP Trackway made by a theropod dinosaur such as *Megalosaurus*.
ABOVE Trackway made by a sauropod dinosaur such as *Cetiosaurus*.

ABOVE A roof tile of Forest Marble. The fossils include scallops, mussels, oysters and the spine of a sea urchin.

ABOVE RIGHT Cornbrash ammonites.
(right) *Clydoniceras*; Lower Cornbrash, Long Hanborough
(left) *Macrocephalites*; Upper Cornbrash, Ducklington Lane, Witney.

BELOW Outcrop map of the Cornbrash.

for the rubbly limestone, or 'brash' that seemed to produce good corn-growing land. Although it is yet another limestone that appears to belong naturally with the Great Oolite group of limestones, it is markedly different in character from the earlier formations and heralds a great change in environment and geography.

Instead of the usual east to west gradation from nearshore to open sea, the Cornbrash is more or less uniform in lithology all the way from Dorset to Yorkshire. The typical rock has a very fine-grained matrix supporting large amounts of shell fragments so that it resembles oat flapjacks. Ooliths are absent and since they are known to be directly precipitated in warm shallow water this suggests that the Cornbrash sea was cooler and deeper.

The fauna bears this out, being more varied than that of the restricted waters of the previous formation. Bryozoa, bivalves and echinoids are common. Brachiopods are especially abundant and ammonites, rare in the rest of the Great Oolite, are not uncommon. These ammonites show that within the apparently uniform Cornbrash there is an important stratigraphical break. *Clydoniceras*, characteristic of the lower part of the formation, is replaced in the upper part by *Macrocephalites*. This form, common in Greenland during Great Oolite times is a newcomer to southern England, migrating from northern seas as deepening water opened new connections

In Oxfordshire the Cornbrash extends from Filkins where the outcrop is a mile and a half wide, through Carterton to Witney. From there the outcrop is narrow as far as Woodstock, where it broadens again to cover some 6 kilometres of the west

0   4 cm

Commonly found bivalves of the Cornbrash Formation.
(left) *Homomya gibbosa*, (right) *Pholadomya deltoidea*; from Kirtlington.

These animals lived buried in the mud of the sea floor, drawing water with oxygen and food particles into the shell through a long tube, or siphon, of soft tissue.

bank of the Cherwell and continues north-eastwards into Buckinghamshire via Middleton Stoney, Bucknell and Fringford, Bicester and Stratton Audley. The limestone is only 2-3 metres thick and is all Lower Cornbrash except for patchy cappings of Upper Cornbrash near the Cherwell Valley.

FIVE

OXFORD CLAY

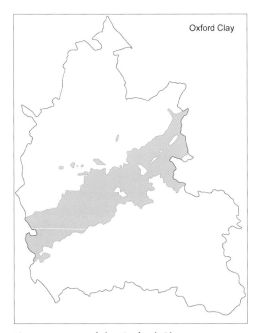

Outcrop map of the Oxford Clay.

Oxford Clay ammonites.
(left) *Kosmoceras*; Lower Oxford Clay, Kidlington
(right) *Cardioceras*; Upper Oxford Clay, Horton-cum-Studley.

The Oxford Clay is so different from the Great Oolite limestones below, and from the sands and limestones of the overlying Corallian Beds, that it is given a little chapter to itself. Furthermore, it spans the boundary between the Middle and Upper Jurassic, which is drawn at the base of the Upper Oxford Clay. At this point there is a marked change in the composition of the ammonite fauna. The kosmoceratid family which had flourished during Lower and Middle Oxford Clay times was completely replaced by cardioceratids whose true home had, until then, been the oceans of the far north.

The sea level rise which began in Cornbrash times produced open sea over most of southern England and beyond. The Oxfordshire shallows were submerged to a depth of several tens of metres, but the London Platform remained either just above sea level or just below it, and was probably the source of some of the mud that was to become the Oxford Clay.

The Oxford Clay proper is preceded by deposits of clay and sand or sandstone called the Kellaways Beds. In Oxfordshire these are very thin – just six metres, for example, at Kidlington – and are rarely exposed.

The Oxford Clay covers a broad tract of low-lying land south-east of a line through Witney, Bicester and Buckingham and underlies Oxford itself. It forms the valley of the upper Thames above Oxford, that of the Cherwell from Kidlington to Oxford, and that of the Ray, including Otmoor. Although widely covered by gravel and **alluvium**, it is often seen in temporary excavations where it appears to be a uniform, sticky, blue-grey clay. In fact, variations in lithology occur throughout the formation, principally in the amount of included organic matter.

The Lower Oxford Clay is rich in carbonaceous organic matter. Freshly dug material splits readily along bedding planes which often reveal the crushed shells of ammonites and bivalves preserved in white or iridescent **aragonite**. The Middle and Upper Oxford Clay are rather calcareous, blocky clays that do not split open in layers, and are less rich in organic

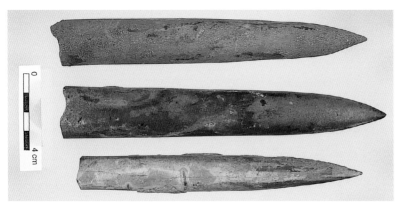

material. Aragonite is not usually preserved and the best known fossils are internal casts of ammonites preserved in gleaming, brassy, **pyrite**.

The temperature of the sea in Lower Oxford Clay times as calculated from **oxygen isotope** ratios, was about 20 degrees C. The fossils show that this comfortable environment was inhabited by a wide range of swimming forms such as ammonites, belemnites, fishes and reptiles while the animals that lived on or in the sea floor, mainly bivalves and gastropods, though less diverse, were abundant in numbers.

Ammonites are common throughout the Oxford Clay and the many different successive forms are the means of stratigraphic subdivision of the formation. Fossil oysters of the genus *Gryphaea* are common at several levels and the upper Oxford Clay species, the large thick-shelled *Gryphaea dilatata*, is so durable that it is frequently seen on fields and in gardens.

A prominent feature of the Lower Oxford Clay is the presence of nodules at certain levels. These nodules, or concretions, are rounded masses of hard rock which can be up to a metre across. They formed a little way down in the mud of the sea floor by chemical reactions involving the decay of

ABOVE LEFT   Oxford Clay belemnites. *Cylindroteuthis puzosiana*; Lower Oxford Clay, Gill Mill, south-west of Witney. The belemnite animal resembled a modern squid. Its body was situated at the end of a thin-walled, chambered, conical shell that fitted into the blunt end of this bullet-shaped shell.

ABOVE   Ammonites preserved in aragonite. *Kosmoceras phaeinum*, Lower Oxford Clay, Gill Mill, south-west of Witney.

BELOW   Ammonites preserved in pyrite. (top row) *Quenstedtoceras*, (bottom row) *Hecticoceras, Distichoceras, Kosmoceras* From Upper Oxford Clay, Stanton Harcourt.

BELOW LEFT   *Gryphaea dilatata*, Upper Oxford Clay, Appleton. The right hand picture shows the inside of the shell made up of many growth layers. The concave area on the top is the hinge. The circular, raised area in the centre is the attachment point for the muscle that closed the two halves of the shell.

41

ABOVE A septarian concretion on display outside the Department of Earth Sciences, Parks Road, Oxford, from the Lower Oxford Clay, near Bicester. The concretion formed in the soft, organic mud of the sea floor. The clay sediment was cemented by calcite and pyrite generated by local bacterial activity. A short time later and a few metres below the sea floor, other chemical changes and dehydration took place resulting in a polygonal pattern of shrinkage cracks. Later still, calcite crystals have grown to fill the cracks.

ABOVE RIGHT The Lower Oxford Clay at Hampton Gorse, north-east of Kidlington. This pit was dug alongside the A34 in 1988 to provide material for widening the road. The freshly dug clay, dark in colour, turns pale blue-grey as it dries. The top 2 metres or so is clay that is deeply weathered and is oxidised to a buff colour.

BELOW Pliosaur skeleton. Lower Oxford Clay, gravel pit at Yarnton.

organic material, such as dead ammonites, and the consequent local formation and accumulation of pyrite and calcite. At some levels the concretions are traversed by a network of cracks which are lined with crystalline calcite. These are known as septarian nodules and are sometimes mistaken for turtle shells. A fine example is on public display outside the Department of Earth Sciences in Parks Road, Oxford.

Because these nodules formed while the Oxford Clay was still being deposited, the fossils that they enclose are preserved three dimensionally. Those in the unconsolidated clay around are crushed flat by subsequent compaction of the sediment. A level of hard, strongly pyritic nodules occurs low down in the Oxford Clay. In the gravel pit at Yarnton in 1994 a nearly complete five metres long skeleton of a pliosaur was found partially enclosed in a group of these nodules. Pliosaurs were reptiles that were completely adapted for life in the sea. The head and jaws were like those of a crocodile, the body broad like a turtle's, and the four limbs modified into paddles for swimming and steering. This skeleton is now on display at the University Museum of Natural History in Parks Road, Oxford.

Other reptiles relatively common in the Lower Oxford Clay include plesiosaurs, ichthyosaurs and crocodiles. Plesiosaurs resembled pliosaurs in their turtle-like body with four paddles, but they had a small head on a long neck. Ichthyosaurs resembled modern dolphins. The Oxford Clay ichthyosaurs are called *Ophthalmosaurus* on account of their very large eyes, up to 25 centimetres in diameter. These are the largest eyes relative to body size of any known vertebrate. Crocodiles include both sea-going forms with a fish-like tail and limbs modified into paddles, as well as coastal, shallow water forms with narrow snouts resembling the modern gavial of the River Ganges.

The most important fossil to come out of the local Oxford Clay is not a contemporary sea creature, but a theropod dinosaur whose corpse must have floated some distance from

Skeleton of the carnivorous dinosaur *Eustreptospondylus oxoniensis* and the restoration of the head of the full-sized animal. The skeleton is of a juvenile a little over 4 metres long and was discovered in the Oxford Clay of a brickpit at Summertown.

land before sinking to the sea bed. The skeleton, almost complete and the only one of its kind, represents an immature individual about four and a half metres long. It has a long, large head and jaws set with blade-like teeth. The short neck and body are balanced by a long, heavy tail. The forelimbs are short and the animal walked on its long hind legs. The bones were found in 1870 in the Summertown brickpit which was located on the Woodstock Road, Oxford, 300 metres south-west of St Edward's School. Now known as *Eustreptospondylus oxoniensis*, this skeleton had, until recently, the distinction of being the only near-complete specimen of a bipedal, carnivorous dinosaur in Europe.

The Summertown brickpit was the largest of several pits in Oxford working the Middle and Upper Oxford Clay. All had closed down by the early 20th century owing to various adverse economic factors, including those caused by the First World War and the development of the Fletton brick industry in Bedfordshire. The Fletton process uses the Lower Oxford Clay, which has the advantages of a low water content, an appropriate calcium carbonate content and a high content of organic matter. The high calorific value of the organic material means that the raw bricks are practically self-firing, needing relatively little fuel to maintain and control the firing temperature of 1000 degrees C.

Scarcely a trace remains of the old brickpits and their informative sections of the Oxford Clay. At present only limited exposures are available in the clay that underlies the gravel being extracted in pits at Cassington near Oxford and around Hardwick in the lower Windrush Valley near Witney.

Outcrop map of the Corallian.

The 11th century tower of St Michael at the Northgate, Oxford. The random rubblestone of the walls is Coral Rag. The squared corner stones and central balusters of the windows are of Taynton Stone from Taynton and Burford.

SIX

UPPER JURASSIC

CORALLIAN FORMATION

The Oxford Clay episode came to an end with a fall of sea level. The Oxford area became part of a region of shallow water in which sand and limestone deposition predominated. These sediments are grouped together as the Corallian Formation, taking the name from one of the best known limestones, the Coral Rag, which contains abundant fossil corals.

These sands and limestones form the cappings of the hills that ring Oxford from Wytham and Cumnor to Headington and Elsfield. They continue north-eastwards as high ground overlooking the Oxford Clay plain via Beckley, Stanton St John and Forest Hill. Just beyond Wheatley the sands and limestones disappear and their place is taken by the Ampthill Clay which was deposited in deeper water.

South-west of Oxford, the Corallian rocks form a low ridge extending from Cumnor to Faringdon and, from there, to Swindon and north Wiltshire. Between Oxford and Faringdon the ridge separates the valley of the upper Thames from the Vale of White Horse, its steep scarp slope facing north towards the Thames and its gentler southerly side sloping down the dip of the strata towards the Ock.

Around Oxford the Corallian rocks comprise 20 metres or so of sand overlain by about 10 metres of limestone. Farther west towards Faringdon the formation is thicker and includes a further sequence of sand and limestones. Within this general scheme there is great variation in rock type from place to place and there are exceptions from the main pattern.

Around Arngrove and Boarstall, for example, there exists a lateral equivalent of the lower sands in the form of a pale grey, porous sandstone, very light in weight, and made up largely of minute siliceous globules that were once the **spicules** of sponges. A wide variety of bivalves are the main fossils, though ammonites are common at some levels (see

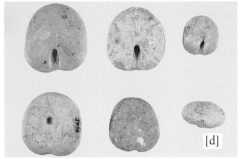

Corallian fossils.
[a] oysters; *Nanogyra nana*, Headington
[b] coral; *Isastrea explanata*, Cumnor
[c] coral; *Thecosmilia annularis*, Mons Way, Abingdon, 1989.
[d] sea urchins; *Nucleolites scutatus*, Cowley.

illustration on page 4). The Arngrove Stone, as it is called, evidently represents an area of relatively stable sea floor colonised by sponges in a clean-water environment, disturbed only by gentle currents bringing in small amounts of sand grains.

Another unusual development is seen in the rocks around Littlemore and Sandford, consisting of alternations of thin beds of clay and muddy limestones with few fossils apart from the small oyster *Nanogyra nana*. The environment must have been a quiet marine lagoon, somehow set apart from the agitated waters of the nearby contemporary coral mounds.

The fossilised remains of the corals which formed a chain of patch reefs fringing the London Platform later on in Corallian times, are preserved as the loosely rubbly limestone known as the Coral Rag. Corals are very common and the best known are the compact 'honeycomb' *Isastrea* and the loosely branching *Thecosmilia*. These can be easily seen in the walls of the old rubble buildings in and around Oxford, such as the tower of St Michael at the Northgate, or in the city walls where the Coral Rag is mixed with pieces of sandstone and shelly limestones from other Corallian beds.

Around the coral mounds banks of lime sand accumulated, made up of the broken shells of molluscs and sea urchins with some coral debris. These sands, now lithified as a series of limestones, are called the Wheatley Limestone after the locality where their thickest development occurs. This stone has been exploited for building stone in a number of quarries around the town. Little is to be seen of them now except for those at Lye Hill, straddling the Forest Hill/Islip turnoff from the A40 Oxford to Wheatley road, where there is still a good section. The fourteenth century was the heyday of the working when stone came not only to Oxford for building Merton, Queen's, Exeter and New College, but also was sent in quantity to Windsor Castle.

The Radcliffe Camera, Oxford, 1737-1747. The white plinth at ground level and at the base of the columns in the upper storey are Headington Hardstone. The channelled ashlar of the lower storey is Headington Freestone. Above, the walls and columns were originally of Taynton Stone but are now much patched with other stones.

Another outcrop of the Wheatley Limestone, closer to Oxford, at Headington, is usually simply called Headington Stone or Headington Freestone. Huge amounts of this stone came to Oxford from the end of the fourteenth century down to the beginning of the nineteenth for high quality buildings. Much of the Headington Stone has decayed badly in Oxford's damp atmosphere which in the past was loaded with coal smoke, and has been replaced with other stones. But much still remains. An excellent example is the channel-jointed ashlar of the lower storey of the Radcliffe Camera. The plinth of whiter stone and the same white stone above forming a plinth for the columns of the upper storey is also from Headington, and is a variant known as Headington Hardstone, or simply, Headington Hard. As the name implies, the stone is hard and durable, although at first sight its often pitted and pock-marked surface suggests an inferior quality. The cavities are due to the weathering-out of softer fillings of burrows which were made by lobster-like crustaceans into the original sediment while it was still firm, but not too hard. A plinth of white Headington Hard and walling of buff Headington

Freestone (or similar replacement) is an attractive feature of traditional Oxford buildings.

The Headington quarries, covering more than 36 hectares (90 acres) of ground, are now built over, but the former activity is evident in the area's surprising dips and hollows, narrow alleys and occasional cottages of Headington **ashlar**.

Nearby, at Rock Edge recreation ground, across Windmill Road from the Nuffield Orthopaedic Hospital, the remains of the Cross Roads Quarry still display up to 3 metres of pale, rubbly limestones with abundant corals and bivalves. The lower parts are shell-fragmental Wheatley Limestone, but higher up, colonies of the corals *Isastrea* and *Thecosmilia*, still in life position, make up most of the rock.

The rich variety of the Corallian rocks in the district can be examined at a number of other sites. In Tubney Wood, some 8 kilometres south-west of Oxford on the road to Swindon, quarries are working the basal Corallian sands, the Lower Calcareous Grit. Here and there the sand is cemented into large masses of hard sandstone, called **doggers**, in which are preserved original features such as animal burrows and ripples.

Two kilometres south-east is the Dry Sandford or Cothill pit. Long abandoned as a working quarry, it has been adopted by the Berkshire, Buckinghamshire and Oxfordshire Wildlife Trust on account of the interesting flora and fauna. The site is important for the species of solitary bees and wasps that nest by burrowing into the weakly cemented Corallian sands.

The base of the old quarry face is a metre or two of coarse sand with doggers. Above it is a thin, impersistent, rubbly,

Quarry in Tubney Wood, south-west of Oxford. Lower Calcareous Grit, Corallian Formation, showing cross-bedding and doggers.

Corallian Beds at Dry Sandford Pit, near Abingdon. Formerly quarried for limestone and sand, the pit is now owned and managed by the Berkshire, Buckinghamshire & Oxfordshire Wildlife Trust, not only for its geological interest but for the rich variety of habitats and wildlife.

Shellingford Quarry, near Faringdon. Two to three metres of Highworth Grit are overlain by a metre or so of coarse-grained limestones and a final couple of metres of rubbly Coral Rag.

pebbly limestone which has yielded an abundant fauna of fossil bivalves and ammonites. Then comes another metre of sand, followed by a metre of platey limestone from which, again, have been collected abundant bivalves, gastropods and ammonites. Next is a little less than a metre of marl with rubbly nodular limestone and an abundance of a small sea urchin called *Nucleolites scutatus*. Finally, at the top of the section is a trace of Coral Rag, rubbly limestone with much coral debris.

Farther west, near Stanford-in-the-Vale, the Shellingford Cross Roads pit was formerly dug for sand, not from the basal Corallian Lower Calcareous Grit, but from the Highworth Grit, an additional sand unit not present in the Oxford area. The overlying 4 metres of oolitic limestones, marls and Coral Rag show a sequence that represents loose lime sands being colonised and stabilised by corals. The top metre or so of Coral Rag has many well preserved corals in life position. A section of the face is preserved as a Site of Special Scientific Interest (SSSI).

The Highworth Grit is better seen in nearby working quarries. Various sedimentary structures in the sands are interpreted as indicating an original environment of sand banks and mud flats subject to tidal currents.

Dozens of smaller quarries all over the Corallian outcrop have now disappeared, but some of the variety of their rocks can be seen in the walls of the local cottages and churches.

The Corallian shallows were gradually drowned as a result of new sea-level rise over southern Britain. The Kimmeridge Clay Formation which follows the Corallian is a series of dark clays, representing the mud that settled out from the deeper, open waters that now covered the region.

At Kimmeridge in Dorset the formation is over 500 metres thick, but it thins north-eastwards, and at Wheatley, which lay near the edge of the basin, it is only 30 metres thick. The outcrop, after crossing Dorset and Wiltshire, enters Oxfordshire at Shrivenham and forms the northern half of the Vale of White Horse. From Abingdon a northward spur underlies Radley, Bagley Wood, Boars Hill and Cumnor Hurst. East of the Thames the Kimmeridge Clay occupies tracts of ground around the hilly areas of the Baldons, Garsington, Shotover and Forest Hill. The outcrop narrows around Tiddington, then widens again from Thame onwards into the Vale of Aylesbury.

The Kimmeridge Clay is by no means a single mass of dark clay. At intervals there are muddy limestones and horizons of nodules. In the upper part of the formation there are silt and sand deposits representing local episodes of shallowing.

The different bodies of sand are known by local names, such as the Shotover Grit Sands, the Wheatley Sands and the Thame Sands. Formerly exploited in numerous pits, the sands are not now well exposed, but can be glimpsed here and there, for example on Shotover, where they contain huge doggers called Giant's Marbles. These sand bodies represent shallow, current-swept, well oxygenated sea floors which supported a rich and diverse fauna of bivalves and gastropods.

Outcrop map of Kimmeridge Clay.

Kimmeridgian palaeogeography.

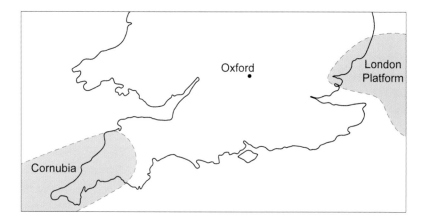

49

A mass of oysters, *Nanogyra virgula*; Lower Kimmmeridge Clay, M40 road excavations, near Waterstock.

Kimmeridge Clay fossils.
[a] Teeth of a pliosaur, *Liopleurodon ferox*, from M40 excavations, Waterstock, 1989.
[b] Vertebra of an ichthyosaur; Chawley Brickpit, Cumnor
[c] Oyster; *Deltoideum delta*,Tilsley Park Sports Ground, Abingdon, 1994.
[d] Vertebra of a plesiosaur; Shotover.

The characteristic fossils in the earliest Kimmeridgian strata are distinctive oysters – the flat, triangular *Deltoideum delta* and the little, striated *Nanogyra virgula*. The main bulk of the clays contain an abundant and varied fauna of bivalves, gastropods and ammonites, along with a range of vertebrates that includes sharks, bony fishes, turtles, ichthyosaurs, plesiosaurs, crocodiles, pterosaurs and even dinosaurs. The great size of many of the bones indicates that this was a time of giants. For example, in the collections at the Oxford University Museum of Natural History, an isolated tail vertebra of a megalosaur-like dinosaur from Shotover is ten percent larger than the corresponding bone of the great Stonesfield *Megalosaurus*. And the lower jaw of a pliosaur from Chawley near Cumnor, at almost 3 metres long, represents an impressive hunter of the Kimmeridgian seas.

Of all the bones that came from the old brick pits of Swindon, Culham, Shotover, Wheatley, Brill and other places, perhaps the most interesting are those of a dinosaur from the Chawley pit at Cumnor, 4 kilometres southwest of Oxford. Discovered by workmen in 1879, the bones were at first thrown aside. Later one of the men took a bag of them down to the University Museum in Oxford where their importance was recognised. The animal, now known as *Camptosaurus prestwichii*, was a herbivorous dinosaur that walked on all fours or on its strong hind legs. It was about 3.5 metres long and the loose connections between the skull bones show that it was still not fully grown when it died and floated out to sea. The skeleton is almost complete, but lacks the hands and ribs.

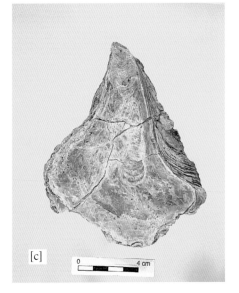

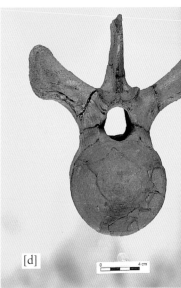

It is the most complete skeleton of the genus (*Camptosaurus*) in Europe and the only specimen of the species. It is on display at the Oxford University Museum of Natural History.

The Kimmeridge Clay is deeply weathered at outcrop and the fresh clay is mostly seen only in temporary exposures, such as deep foundation trenches or pipelines. The only semi-permanent exposures in the district are the floors of the gravel pits around Abingdon.

Restoration of the herbivorous dinosaur *Camptosaurus prestwichii* by Gareth Monger, based on the unique skeleton found at Chawley brickpit in 1879. The bones represent an immature individual about three and a half metres long.

PORTLAND FORMATION

The end of Kimmeridgian times and the beginning of the Portlandian was marked by a widespread fall in sea level over southern England. For the next five million years or so Oxford lay in shallow water in a strait linking an East Midlands basin of deposition with a series of basins over Wessex and the Channel and close to the emergent London Platform.

The Portlandian deposits of the Oxford area are represented by less than 13 metres of sand and limestone. In contrast, in Dorset, in the Isle of Portland and in Purbeck, there are 70 metres of beds, including the white building stone made famous by its extensive use in the rebuilding of London after the Great Fire of 1666.

Portland Beds also appear in the Vale of Wardour, on the hilltop of old Swindon and of nearby Bourton, but those of Oxfordshire and Buckinghamshire are the most northerly and the most extensive in England. They make up the higher parts of Shotover Hill, east of Oxford city, and of the hilly ground around Wheatley, Cuddesdon, Garsington and Toot Baldon. To the south-east, across the River Thame, they outcrop more widely around the Miltons and Haseleys.

In Buckinghamshire, Portland Beds form a wide tract of

Outcrop map of Portlandian.

Brill Windmill. The hollows and hummocky ground are the remains of old diggings for clay, sand and building stone from the Portland and Purbeck beds.

BELOW Portlandian bivalves.
(top left) *Myophorella incurva*, Great Milton
(top right) *Trigonia gibbosa*, Brill
(below) *Protocardia dissimilis*, Shotover.
The two fossils on the left are internal moulds. The original shell has dissolved away leaving a natural impression of its inner surface on the sediment inside.

BELOW RIGHT Portlandian ammonite, *Galbanites*, Brill.

ground between Thame and Aylesbury, south of the Thame. North of the river they occur extensively in the range of hills stretching from Long Crendon to Waddesdon, and in the outlying mass of Brill.

There are no longer any quarries in the district where the Portland Beds can be studied, but the records of many former small workings demonstrate a general sequence of sands with some rubbly, sandy limestones beneath an upper set of limestones. The sands are characterised, in the lower parts, by abundant green and black grains of **glauconite**, a mineral rich

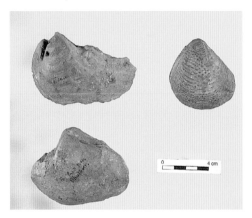

in iron and potassium. At outcrop the glauconite is broken down by weathering, releasing ochreous iron oxides and giving rise to brown, loamy soils.

The fossil fauna of the Portland Beds is rich in large bivalves and is renowned for its giant ammonites. Specimens of half a metre or more in diameter are not uncommon and are often seen as garden ornaments or as features built into walls. Those in the wall of Hartwell Park, a couple of kilometres southwest of Aylesbury will be familiar to all travellers along the road from Thame.

The Upper Portland beds, or Creamy Limestones, around Great and Little Milton and Great and Little Haseley, contain a bed of building stone up to two metres thick. This sandy limestone was formerly dug as a freestone for local buildings from many small quarries.

PURBECK FORMATION

The sands and limestones of the Portland Formation are the last fully marine sediments of the Jurassic. The overlying clays, sands and limestones of the Purbeck Formation are of a different character. They exhibit a range of features such as algal mats (indicating very shallow or intertidal water), shrinkage cracks (indicating exposure of the sediment to the air), and beds full of tiny crustaceans called ostracods (indicating waters of variable salinities). The beds were evidently laid down in shallow, coastal or lagoonal environments.

The regional evidence of the rocks provides a palaeogeographical picture in which the continued fall in sea level had caused the shallows of the Wessex and Weald basin to become almost landlocked. From time to time the sea made temporary incursions, flooding the region and altering the salinity of the waters.

On the Isle of Purbeck, in Dorset, which gives its name to the formation, the rocks include fossil soils and the remains of forests, as well as excellent building stones. The Purbeck Marble, widely used as a decorative stone in mediaeval cathedrals and churches is well known. It is a dark, muddy limestone packed with the little shells of a freshwater snail. Evidence from the rings in the wood of fossil trees suggests a rather dry, Mediterranean-type climate with rain falling mainly in the winter.

Purbeckian palaeogeography.

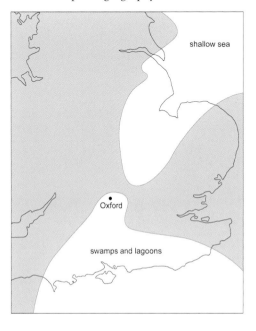

shallow sea

Oxford

swamps and lagoons

53

Great Milton church; walling of local Portlandian limestone.

Around Oxford, located at the northern end of the great tract of shallow lakes and mudflats, little sediment accumulated and that little was reduced by erosion in early Cretaceous times. As a result, only minor remnants are still present, found mainly near Great and Little Milton. The most extensive patches are in Buckinghamshire between Haddenham and Stone, and on the hills to the north-west, such as Long Crendon and Brill. The only place where any of the rocks can be seen, apart from temporary exposures, is in the Bugle Pit SSSI at Hartwell near Aylesbury, where three metres or so of sands and splintery limestones are visible.

SEVEN

THE LOWER CRETACEOUS

The Cretaceous Period began 144 million years ago when the late Jurassic phase of earth movements turned most of north-west Europe into land. Early in the period the climate began to warm. It reached greenhouse conditions in the mid Cretaceous, with atmospheric levels of carbon dioxide up to 10 times those of the present time, and then cooled towards the end of the Period. The rise in carbon dioxide resulted from increased volcanic activity in the Pacific which also produced much new sea floor. This increased volume of rock raised sea levels worldwide.

The early earth movements, however, raised the London Platform well above sea level, exposing the Jurassic sediments to the weather. Their erosion supplied huge amounts of mud and sand to the swamps and lagoons of the Weald basin of Surrey, Sussex and Kent and, eventually, small quantities to the Oxford area. By the Upper Cretaceous this activity had died down and the whole region was covered by sea in which a blanket of chalky ooze began to be deposited.

LOWER CRETACEOUS

In Oxfordshire the earliest Cretaceous rocks are the deposits that cap Shotover and the ridge between Wheatley and Garsington. They are predominantly fine- to medium-grained sands, frequently rich in iron. These characteristics gave rise to the old names of Shotover Sands and Shotover Iron Sands. However, these horizons are now considered to be equivalent to the Whitchurch Sands of Buckinghamshire and are included in that formation.

Further patches of these Lower Cretaceous beds occur around the Miltons and Haseleys and cap Brill and Muswell Hills as well as many other small hills between Brill and Aylesbury. Across the district they lie on various levels of the underlying Portland and Purbeck beds, which implies that a period of erosion preceded their deposition. The available

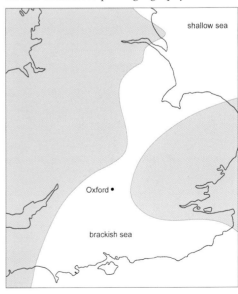

Lower Cretaceous palaeogeography.

Shotover Ironsand, (Whitchurch Sand Formation), with internal moulds of the bivalve *Unio sp.* (The red paint has been applied to clarify internal structures.)

evidence from fossils correlates the Whitchurch Sands with levels in the complete sequence of the Weald that were laid down between seven and ten million years after the end of the Jurassic

Evidence for the climate of this time comes from the clay mineral kaolinite, which has a substantial presence in the Whitchurch Sands. Kaolinite is regarded as a product of weathering in acid soils in a warm climate with high rainfall. In contrast, in the late Jurassic sediments, kaolinite is rare and supporting evidence from tree rings suggests that the climate at that time was rather arid and strongly seasonal.

On Shotover, where the formation is thickest, there are nearly 20 metres of sands, clay seams and ironstones. The sands are grey, white, yellow or brown according to the amount of iron oxides present. Seams of silt and clay that are rich in brown and yellow oxides were formerly dug for ochre. According to Robert Plot's book, *The Natural History of Oxfordshire* (1677), the ochre 'is accounted the best of its kind in the world . . . much used by painters simply of itself . . . '. Plot also writes that a seam of white clay on Shotover was used for making tobacco pipes during the 1640s. The highest strata are ferruginous sands, so rich in iron as to form hard, flaggy, purple-brown ironstone. This stone was dug for iron ore at a pit near Wheatley for a short time in the late nineteenth century

No pits are now open, but the old records describe lithological features in the sands and ironstones such as cross-bedding and channels, that indicate deposition in a river. Fossil wood is fairly common. A fossil tree, 12 metres long, was found in the 1830s at Brill. The ironstones preserve a few fossils of freshwater molluscs such as the gastropod *Viviparus* and the freshwater mussel *Unio*. However, in the middle of the sequence is a thin band of rock that has yielded a few marine fossils including a nautiloid, a sea urchin and some scallops. This episode is possibly contemporaneous with the marine incursion in Russia which is taken as the boundary between the Jurassic and Cretaceous

THE LOWER GREENSAND

Around 114 million years ago, and some 20 million years after the time of the Whitchurch Sands, the sea returned to southern England. It advanced in a series of pulses, north-eastwards from the Wessex basin and south-westwards from the North Sea basin. The two marine areas eventually established a connection by a tidally-swept strait along the northern and western edges of the London Platform, from Bedfordshire to Wiltshire. The characteristic deposits are reddish-brown, ferruginous, coarse sands and pebbly sands. The green grains of glauconite from which the formation takes its name are usually only seen in the unweathered rock. The outcrops have a patchy distribution owing to erosion soon after deposition and during the development of the modern landscape.

In Oxfordshire the chief occurrences of the Lower Greensand are found at Faringdon and Baulking; between Culham and Nuneham Courtenay; Boars Hill and Cumnor Hurst near Oxford; and around Tiddington east of Wheatley.

At Faringdon the formation is unusually thick and consists of some 20 metres of the famous sponge-gravels overlain by about a further 30 metres of sands. The outcrop extends in a southerly direction to Baulking and Uffington. Mapping shows that the sediments are filling a trough or channel. This was scoured out by a marine current that cut into the seabed of Kimmeridgian and Corallian rocks. The limestones and other hard bands thus exposed were colonised by a rich fauna of sponges and bryozoans with associated brachiopods, oysters and sea urchins. Occasional storms ripped up sponges and bryozoans and mixed them with coarse pebbly sand and with fossils derived from the underlying Jurassic beds to form

Lower Greensand outcrop.

57

ABOVE AND ABOVE RIGHT Two views of the Lower Greensand Red Sponge Gravels, Wicklesham Pit, Faringdon.

BELOW Sponges from Wicklesham Pit. (from top left) *Raphidonema farringdonense, Elasmocoelia faringdonensis, Corynella foraminosa.*

These are representatives of a group of sponges which have a rigid calcareous skeleton made up of tiny, interlocking spicules often shaped like tuning forks. (note; the two different spellings of Faringdon are correct in this context).

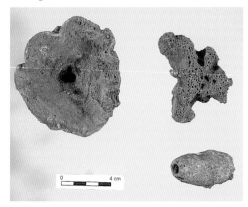

sand banks that now make up the Faringdon Sponge Gravels.

At Wicklesham Pit, just south-east of the town, the Gravels are still worked for sand and aggregates. The section shows some 8 metres of gravel, stained deep red with iron oxide and packed with the remains of sponges and other invertebrates. The derived Jurassic fossils include rolled and blackened remnants of ammonites and bivalves, as well as bones and teeth of sharks, ichthyosaurs, plesiosaurs and giant crocodiles.

On the town side of the bypass in Fernham Road is the old Coxwell Pit, now an SSSI. The side of the worked out quarry is a 4 metre high wall of yellow gravel, even more fossiliferous than the red Wicklesham gravel.

At Baulking, 6 kilometres south-east of Faringdon, the sands of the upper part of the sequence include two seams of fuller's earth clay. This clay has absorbent properties that make it valuable for certain industrial applications, including use with foundry sands, in paper making and in fertiliser-pelleting. Although the better of the seams was little more than a metre and a half thick at the most, the material is scarce enough to be worth extracting and has now been worked out. New seams in the area have been located by drilling and are to be exploited. Geologically the seams are interesting because fuller's earth is formed from the decomposition of volcanic ash in a marine environment. Volcanic vents of appropriate age are known from the Netherlands and from the North Atlantic.

Another patch of Lower Greensand lies to the east of Abingdon, bounded by Culham, Nuneham Courtenay and Burcot. On the Abingdon loop of the Thames it forms the steep wooded banks of Nuneham Park and the cliff at Clifton Hampden. At Nuneham the sands account for the acidic soil on which rhododendrons flourish in the University Arboretum.

At Culham the coarse sands are patchily cemented by calcium carbonate into hard masses which have provided material for querns from the Iron Age to medieval times.

Remnants of the Culham-Nuneham mass, now detached by weathering, are represented by the coarse red sands that form the capping of the Boars Hill range between Sunningwell and Cumnor.

One further patch of Lower Greensand occurs around Tiddington, some 10 or 12 kilometres east of Oxford. Boring has proved up to 16 metres of red sands similar to those overlying the Sponge Gravels at Faringdon.

GAULT AND UPPER GREENSAND FORMATIONS

The continuing rise in sea level progressively flooded most of southern England and northwest Europe and eventually submerged the London Platform. With land sediment sources now distant, only finer particles of silt and clay reached the sea floor. Their accumulation formed the Gault Clay, which now appears as a narrow belt from Wiltshire to Bedfordshire.

In Oxfordshire the Gault Clay makes a low-lying tract of land four or five kilometres wide parallel with the escarpment of the Downs and Chilterns. It forms the southern half of the Vale of the White Horse from Uffington to Wantage. East of there it is largely covered by gravel but reappears at the surface as a broad arc around the north-east side of Didcot. Across the Thames it emerges from under the gravel at Warborough and passes by Chalgrove, Stadhampton and Tetsworth, then south and south-east of Thame into Buckinghamshire.

The Gault is a grey, sometimes silty, clay, characteristically with bands of nodules and thin layers of black pebbles. These black stones represent periods when currents acted on the sea floor, winnowing the sediment and exhuming fossils from earlier layers. As the fossils rolled around the sea bed they absorbed phosphate from the water to form dark-coloured calcium phosphate.

These black stones were commonly known as coprolites, from their superficial resemblance to the coprolites, or fossilised droppings of ichthyosaurs, from the Lower Lias at Lyme Regis. At some places the layers, though little more than a few centimetres thick, were nevertheless rich enough in phosphate to be worth digging for conversion to fertiliser. During the second half of the 19th century pits were opened at

Outcrop map of Gault and Upper Greensand.

ABOVE Wittenham Clumps from the east. The hills are made of Malmstone with a capping of Lower Chalk. Gault Clay forms the level foreground and the land around Didcot Power Station.

BELOW RIGHT Thame; bricks from Gault Clay.

Towersey near Thame and at several other places in Buckinghamshire and Bedfordshire.

The Gault Clay provided the material for many fine brick buildings along the outcrop. Some of the more important brickpits were those at Uffington, Childrey, Culham, Chalgrove and Thame.

While the Gault Clay was being deposited in the Oxford area, a mass of higher ground over Cornwall was supplying sand to the western part of the basin. These sands, commonly

speckled with glauconite are the Upper Greensand Formation. In Oxfordshire the sands of the west are represented by a pale, fine-grained, lightweight rock called Malmstone. Although it looks like Chalk, Malmstone is a type of sandstone, largely made up of grains of silica derived from the spicules of sponges. It forms the noticeable scarp and shelf up to a kilometre and a half wide at the foot of the main rise of the Downs and Chilterns from Woolstone, by Kingston Lisle, Wantage, the Hendreds, Harwell, Didcot, North Moreton, Brightwell Baldwin, Postcombe and Sydenham. It forms the main bulk of the Sinodun Hills near Dorchester and the steep bank of the Thames at Wallingford.

A number of springs issue from the base of the Malmstone where the porous rock grades down into the clay of the Gault. Many have cut back into the hillside to form narrow, steep-sided valleys, as at Sparsholt, Childrey, Cuxham and at Henton and Bledlow near Chinnor. At Bledlow and elsewhere the streams fed by these springs have been used for watercress cultivation.

An unusual ammonite from the Malmstone. *Anisoceras armatus*; Roke, near Watlington.

61

EIGHT

THE UPPER CRETACEOUS

Outcrop map of Chalk.

Coccoliths in Chalk. The width of the picture represents 0.025 mm. The minute, calcareous plates of these algae form the main bulk of the Chalk.

The Upper Cretaceous is practically synonymous with the Chalk, the distinctive white rock of the Downs and Chilterns that form the southern and south-western borders of the county. The Chalk is a soft, fine-grained type of limestone, largely composed of minute calcite crystals derived from the disintegration of the skeletons of tiny, floating algae. Each alga, 4,000 of which would fit on the head of a pin, is a spherical cell encased in overlapping plates of calcite called coccoliths. Today coccoliths are characteristic of deep oceanic environments, but in the Upper Cretaceous coccoliths and coccolith dust blanketed vast areas of Europe as the rising sea progressively flooded the continental interior, reaching as far as the present day Aral Sea in Central Asia.

The rise in sea level, probably up to as much as 300 metres above the modern level, is attributed to the welling up of vast quantities of volcanic rock in the floor of the growing North Atlantic Ocean and in the south-east Pacific, which displaced immense volumes of water.

In Oxfordshire, the Chalk escarpment of the Downs presents a steep face to the north, usually consisting of two steps. It reaches a height of 261 metres (856 feet) at White Horse Hill, the highest point in Oxfordshire. From the crest the land sinks gently southwards into Berkshire as an open landscape of rounded ridges and shallow dry valleys.

The face of the Chilterns, which reaches 244 metres (800 feet) near Stokenchurch, is equally steep and also stepped. From Wallingford to Henley the outcrop of the Chalk is 16 kilometres wide. In contrast to the Downs, the Chiltern country is well wooded. This is not because of any difference in the Chalk, but results from the deeper soils provided by spreads of more recent sands, gravels and clays.

The Chalk may appear to be the same white rock everywhere, but within the 240 or so metres of the sequence there are many variations in character that reflect changes in climate, geography and depth of water. These variations, along with the succession of different fossils, are used as the means

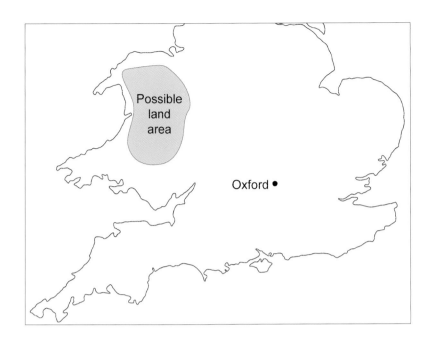

of division into smaller stratigraphical units. The principal divisions are the Lower, Middle and Upper Chalk Formations. The Lower Chalk is a grey, impure, clayey chalk with no flint. In Oxfordshire, the Middle Chalk is white chalk without flint. The Upper Chalk is pure white chalk with abundant flint.

Late Cretaceous palaeogeography.

The Lower Chalk at Childrey, near Wantage.

	Oxfordshire strata	approx thickness in metres
Upper Chalk	White Chalk with flints	65
	Chalk Rock	1
Middle Chalk	White Chalk without flints	65
	Melbourn Rock	4
Lower Chalk	Plenus Marls	1
	Grey Chalk	25
	Totternhoe Stone	1
	Chalk Marl	35
	Glauconitic Marl	1-2

Subdivisions of the Chalk.

The Lower Chalk forms the gentler lower slopes of the Chilterns making a shelf 2 kilometres or more wide on which Chinnor, Kingston Blount, Lewknor and Shirburn are built. A similar shelf is made by Lower Chalk in front of the Downs. Small outlying remnants cap the Sinodun Hills near Dorchester.

Four divisions of the Lower Chalk are generally recognisable. The lowest, the Glauconitic Marl, only 1-2 metres thick, is described by the name of the mineral it contains. In places it gives rise to a markedly greenish, loamy soil. Above it the Chalk Marl is between 25 and 40 metres thick and shows well developed rhythmic bedding. Each rhythmic unit typically comprises a pair of beds, 30-70 cm thick. The lower one contains up to 30% of clay and grades upwards into the upper bed of purer chalk, which is often rich in sponge remains. The rhythms can be traced from England into France and Germany. Their origin is attributed to oscillations of climate due to periodic variations in the earth's orbit, in particular the approximately 20,000 year frequency of precessional cycles. Precession is the rotation of the earth's axis moving in a circle like the wobble of a spinning-top. This affects the pattern of solar radiation received by the earth which in turn produces climatic effects. Changes in rainfall affect the amount of clay carried into depositional basins. Analysis of oxygen isotopes from these rocks indicate that the clayey beds correspond to lower temperatures while the paler, chalkier beds correspond to warmer phases.

Many levels in the Chalk Marl are fossiliferous, yielding a rich fauna of ammonites, bivalves, brachiopods, sponges and

Ammonites from the Lower Chalk.
[a] *Mariella lewesiensis*, Chinnor. Although the shell is helically coiled like that of a gastropod it is also divided by internal cross walls into a series of chambers connected by a thin tube. These are characteristics of ammonites.
[b] *Schloenbachia varians*, Uffington.

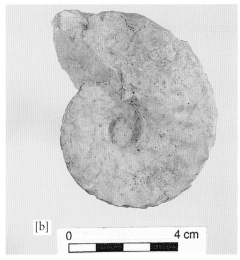

ABOVE *Inoceramus sp*. A bivalve from the Chalk Marl, Chinnor.

ABOVE RIGHT Pyrite nodules from the lower Chalk. In the lower specimen the nodule is broken across to show the radiating crystals of brassy, unweathered pyrite. In the upper specimen the ends of the crystals give the surface a knobbly texture and weathering has produced a red coating of iron oxides.

fish remains. Ammonites include the giant *Austiniceras*, up to a metre and a half across, and the helically coiled, or screw-shaped, *Mariella*.

Not uncommon in the Chalk Marl are heavy, metallic-looking nodules, about the size and shape of potatoes, made of a mass of long narrow crystals radiating from the centre of the nodule. People often suppose them to be meteorites, but in fact they originated by chemical reactions around decaying organic matter in the mud of the Cretaceous sea floor and the crystals are iron sulphide, either **pyrite** or **marcasite**.

At several levels there are bands of harder, strongly cemented chalk. The rigidity of this rock makes it prone to fracture. The cracks facilitate the movement of water so that the bands act as aquifers within the relatively impermeable Chalk Marl. They give rise to springs such as those that feed the watercress beds at Ewelme, East Ginge, Lockinge and Letcombe Bassett.

The most widely developed hard band in the Lower Chalk is the Totternhoe Stone, which comes in above the Chalk Marl and forms the base of the succeeding Grey Chalk. It takes its name from a village near Dunstable in Bedfordshire where the rock is up to 6.5 metres thick and has been worked as a building stone. In the Chilterns it is generally less than a metre and west of the Thames near Chilton, it dies out altogether. It is a brownish, sandy, fossiliferous stone that feels gritty to the touch owing to the abundance of shell fragments, mainly from the bivalve *Inoceramus*.

The rest of the Grey Chalk, some 25 metres thick, is less

clayey than the Chalk Marl and the rhythmic bedding is less well developed. Some beds contain pyrite nodules up to 10 cm long, but fossils are uncommon. At the top is a metre or so of beds that are noticeably different in colour. This yellowish or greenish chalk is called the Plenus Marl, after the characteristic, though not abundant, belemnite, *Actinocamax plenus*. The Plenus Marls extend over southern England and into the continent. The clay content of the beds represents a fall in sea level.

The proportions of clay and lime in the Lower Chalk make it an ideal raw material for the manufacture of cement. It was exploited for this purpose at Chinnor and although production has now ceased, part of the quarry has been designated as an SSSI where almost the whole of the Lower Chalk succession can be studied.

THE MIDDLE AND UPPER CHALK FORMATIONS

In Oxfordshire the Middle Chalk consists mainly of pure white chalk with no flint and is about 65 metres thick. The base is marked by a band of hard, porcelain-like, nodular rock about 4 metres thick, called the Melbourn Rock, after the village in Cambridgeshire where it was first described. It can be examined in the SSSI quarry at Chinnor where it grades up into another 8 metres of softer, less nodular Middle Chalk.

The Upper Chalk comprises some 40 metres of white chalk with bands and nodules of flint. Again, a band of hard rock marks the base. This is the Chalk Rock, about 1 metre thick in the Chilterns, increasing to 3 to 6 metres in the Downs. It consists of nodular chalk mottled green and brown by stains of glauconite and phosphate. This is a complex bed comprising a sequence of half a dozen hard surfaces which represent temporary breaks in sedimentation, during which nodule formation and cementation of the sea floor took place. The outcrop of the Chalk Rock is often marked by the remains of small pits where it was once dug for stone to mend the roads, for example, between the hillfort and the Horse on White Horse Hill.

In the Chilterns the steep slopes of the upper part of the escarpment are formed of Middle Chalk capped by Chalk Rock. From the crest, the higher ground is made by the Upper Chalk along with extensive overlying deposits of clay and gravels of younger age.

OPPOSITE PAGE
TOP View north from White Horse Hill. The
White Horse is in Middle Chalk. Dragon
Hill, left foreground, is in Lower Chalk.
Uffington, in the centre of the picture, is on
Gault Clay. The ridge beyond is the Corallian
outcrop. Left of centre, on the ridge, is
Faringdon Folly in the clump of trees on a
hillock made of Lower Greensand. Behind
the ridge lies the upper Thames valley, its far
wall on the horizon formed by the limestones
of the Great Oolite.
BOTTOM White Horse Hill.

In the M40 road cutting through the Chiltern scarp at Aston Rowant the first 300 metres of white chalk from the Oxford end are the Middle Chalk. The rest of the cutting is Upper Chalk with bands of flint.

The road emerges from the top of the cutting and runs past Stokenchurch where the view opens to the south into the valley which runs for 11 kilometres past Fingest and Hambleden to join the Thames between Henley and Medmenham. This valley and its more westerly branch past Turville cut deeply through the Upper Chalk, forming windows into the Middle Chalk which lines the bottom and lower slopes. A similar valley system, narrow and steep-walled, begins three kilometres west of Turville and runs southwards for nine kilometres by Stonor, Assendon and the Fair Mile to Henley.

Between the Chilterns and the Downs is the Goring Gap – the picturesque gorge cut by the Thames through the Chalk escarpment from Cholsey to Pangbourne. From Cholsey at the northern end the Gap is entered by a funnel-like mouth. On the western side the Downs drop down to the river as a series of steep-sided spurs between Moulsford and Streatley. The floor of the main valley and the side coombes is Lower Chalk while the steep slopes are Middle Chalk. The Chalk Rock forms the edge of the plateau. The southerly dip of the strata gradually brings higher levels of the Chalk towards the valley bottom. The cuttings on the railway line demonstrate the sequence. The first, south of Cholsey is in Lower Chalk. The line then swings across the river and enters the second cutting as it approaches Goring. Lower Chalk is again seen for the first half kilometre or so but is then succeeded by Yellowish Middle Chalk. From Goring the line again crosses the river and between Basildon and Pangbourne it lies in a deep cutting in the flinty Upper Chalk. The clearest exposure is seen in the vertical section on the north side just before Pangbourne station. The bands of black flints stand out sharply against the pure white chalk.

West of the Goring Gap the Downs rise to White Horse Hill. Surprisingly, the impressive height of the hill is mainly in Lower and Middle Chalk, while Upper Chalk accounts only for the top 5 or 6 metres. The Dragon Mound is all Lower Chalk. The White Horse itself, fashioned nearly 3000 years ago by people of the late Bronze or early Iron Age, is cut in the upper part of the Middle Chalk. The Iron Age fort on the summit, Uffington Castle, is in the Upper Chalk.

In the villages at the foot of the Downs, for example,

Flint as a building stone. Chinnor church.

A sea urchin and flint nodule. Flints are often seen to have formed around fossils. The bacterial activity around dead animals would have locally affected the chemistry of sea water in such a way as to allow the precipitation of silica and the growth of a flint nodule.

Woolstone, Uffington, and Kingston Lisle, many old buildings are made with large blocks of fine white Chalk which seems to have come from somewhere in the top of the Lower Chalk and may be the overlying Melbourn Rock. Kept dry by 'good shoes and a hat', that is with a plinth of sarsen stone (see Chapter 9) and overhanging eaves, this chalk has resisted the weather for centuries.

Flint from the Upper Chalk is also an important building material. Flint is a black or grey glassy mineral made up of microscopic crystals of silica. It occurs mainly as irregular nodules with a white crust or patina, concentrated into layers roughly 1 metre apart throughout the Upper Chalk. This striking regularity is ascribed to the climatic cycles caused by variations in the earth's orbit with periodicities of about 21,000, 40,000 and 100,000 thousand years.

LEFT & BELOW   Flint walling at Watlington.

FORMATION OF FLINT

Flint nodules formed within the sediment of the sea floor where the local chemical environment favoured the replacement of chalk by silica. The silica present in solution in the pore water of the sediment came fom the dissolved spicules of siliceous sponges which were abundant in the Chalk sea.

Silica precipitates in acidic conditions whereas these cause calcium carbonate to dissolve. Local acidity would have been associated with decaying organic matter located near the boundary between anaerobic and aerobic levels in the sediment. Such conditions occurred around dead animals such as sea urchins and sponges and especially in the burrow systems of lobster-like arthropods. These burrows, which are extremely common in the Chalk, consist of irregular, horizontal networks of tubes 1 to 10 centimetres in diameter, originally filled with loose sediment and faecal pellets. Growth of silica in and around the burrows is reflected in the branched, horned and knobbly shapes of flints.

NINE

THE TERTIARY

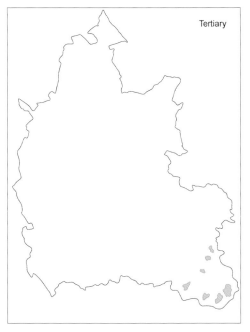

Outcrop map of Tertiary beds.

The end of Cretaceous times was marked by increased movements in the earth's crust, intense volcanic activity and a worldwide fall in sea level. Vast tracts of new land emerged, oceanic circulation was restructured and climatic patterns were altered. Changes on this scale hastened changes in global faunas.

Ichthyosaurs and plesiosaurs had already gone from the seas and now the last ammonites and belemnites, once so diverse and abundant, disappeared forever. The dinosaurs which had dominated the continents for over 150 million years finally petered out and ceded the land to the mammals.

The new **Era** which includes all the time between the end of the Cretaceous Period, 65 million years ago, and the present day, is called the Cenozoic. This name, from the Greek meaning recent life, highlights the more modern aspect of post-Cretaceous faunas. The Cenozoic is divided into the Tertiary and Quaternary Periods. The Quaternary represents only the last two and a half million years and comprises the Pleistocene Ice Age and the interglacial period of the last 10,000 years.

Throughout the greater part of the Cenozoic Oxfordshire was a land area. Erosion has been the principal geological agent in shaping the modern landscape. Earth movements which turned Oxfordshire into dry land began in the late Cretaceous and recurred as pulses during the Tertiary, mainly in the early Tertiary and in the Miocene. The cause of movement was the pressure of the northward-moving African **Plate** (*see chapter 12*) against the Eurasian Plate. The effects included the building of the Alps as well as the uplift of southern England with folding of the Jurassic and Cretaceous strata and the gentle south-easterly tilting of Oxfordshire. During the Tertiary Oxfordshire moved 8 degrees northwards to its present latitude.

The physical situation of Oxfordshire in Tertiary times was the opposite of that during the Jurassic and Cretaceous. Then, it had generally been in the shallows just west of the London Platform with deepening sea farther to the west. Tertiary earth movements altered the physiography so that Oxfordshire was now on the south-eastern edge of a land area and the old London Platform was depressed into a basin. Through much of Tertiary time the rivers draining the land deposited gravels, sands and muds to the south and south-east of the Oxford area. These sediments record the ups and downs of the sea and the shifting back and forth of estuaries, coastal plains and shorelines.

For the first six million years of the Tertiary, erosion was at work in Oxfordshire, wearing down the thick blanket of Chalk. About 59 million years ago sands and clays were deposited in the Reading region in a system of marshy mud flats crossed by river channels. Their extent in Oxfordshire has been reduced by later erosion to remnant patches on top of the Chilterns, mainly around Stonor, Russell's Water, Nettlebed, Nuffield, Stoke Row, Greenmoor and Caversham.

These outcrops of the **Reading Formation** have long provided sand for building and clay for tiles, bricks and pottery. The best known and most extensive workings were at Nettlebed where the clays of the Reading Formation, here over 15 metres thick, were dug in dozens of small pits. The earliest documented notices of workings are dated 1365, when 35,000 tiles were made for Wallingford Castle, and 1416 when 200,000 bricks were produced for Stonor House. The industry lasted into the 20th century; the last bricks were made in 1927.

About a million years of deposition of the Reading Beds was followed by a similar period of erosion. Then another change in sea level brought an arm of the North Sea to flood the London basin. The mud that built up on this sea bottom for the next five million years or so now forms the London Clay. The clay beds are up to 150 metres thick below London, but thin to about 90 metres at Reading, to about 30 metres at Newbury, and disappear altogether in Wiltshire.

Although the only occurrence of London Clay in Oxfordshire is a metre or two of clay on top of the Reading Beds at Nettlebed, the formation as a whole yields interesting information about the environment of the time. As well as the marine fossils there are remains of over 500 species of plants, including mangroves, palms, magnolias, dogwoods, laurel, cinnamon and bay. These give a picture of a warm, equable climate and a lush, forested landscape bordered by a swampy coastal plain.

The most easily observed rock formation of Tertiary age in Oxfordshire occurs as scattered blocks known as sarsen

Sarsens, near Ashdown House, south-west Oxfordshire. These blocks are the remains of Tertiary Beds of sand which became consolidated by silica deposited from groundwater drawn up by evaporation in a warm climate.

stones. Sarsens are white or grey, very dense hard sandstone. They are distributed irregularly over the Chilterns and the Downs of Oxfordshire and Wiltshire. The best places to see them in their natural state are in the valley near Ashdown House in the far south-west of the county, or at Fyfield Down near Marlborough. Originally, spreads of sarsens must have been more extensive, but down the centuries great numbers of them have been cleared from the surface for use as building stone. The standing stones of the Avebury Circle and the huge trilithons of Stonehenge provide impressive examples. In contrast, many farmhouses and cottages were built of small pieces of broken up sarsens.

The sands from which sarsens formed were originally deposited in rivers or lakes, possibly as outlying parts of the Reading Beds. The process that cemented and hardened the sands took place later in the Tertiary, though exactly when is not clear. The process itself is not well understood, but comparison with modern equivalents of sarsens provides some clues. Sarsens may have formed when evaporation from the surface drew groundwater through the sands that formed part of the land surface in an arid or semi-arid climate. Further evaporation caused silica in the groundwater to be deposited

in the pore spaces of the sand, where it built up to form a strong, dense cement.

For the rest of the Tertiary after London Clay times Oxfordshire remained as dry land. During this period of 50 or so million years the pre-existing rocks were weathered and eroded. Also during this time the main effects of the pressure of the African Plate pushing northwards against the European Plate were felt. Although Oxfordshire was affected by little more than a gentle tilt to the south-east, more dramatic effects can be seen, for example, in crumpled rocks at Lulworth Cove and Stair Hole in Dorset, or in the vertical beds of coloured sands of Alum Bay in the Isle of Wight.

Broken up Sarsen forming the plinth below Chalk walling. Woolstone, near Uffington.

TEN

THE QUATERNARY

The latest chapter of geological time, the Quaternary Period, spans the last two million years or so. Most of that time is referred to the Pleistocene Epoch, often called the Ice Age, since during this interval huge ice sheets repeatedly invaded Britain and the northern continents. The retreat of the ice to more or less its present extent about 10,000 years ago marks the beginning of the Holocene Epoch, the warm period in which we are living.

During the relatively brief span of Quaternary time the landscape of Oxfordshire was sculpted into its present form by powerful erosional forces due to climatic extremes. It is also the period when modern people originated and came to occupy northern Europe and Britain.

PLEISTOCENE

The sediments deposited on land during the Pleistocene present a discontinuous, incomplete and complicated record of events. By contrast, the sedimentary record in the oceans is more or less continuous and complete. Contained within the deep sea muds are the shells of tiny organisms called foraminifera. The chemistry of these shells throughout the sequence shows variations that are related to changes in the temperature of the sea water over time. The sequence of variations shows that the Pleistocene was not a single cold period, but that fluctuations between cold and warm intervals occurred some fifty times.

During the coldest phases, or glacials, conditions in Britain were cold enough for arctic environments to develop, while in the milder, interglacials, temperatures were occasionally higher than those of the present day. In the last 800,000 years, the period for which there is substantial evidence in onshore Britain, there have been three principal glacial periods, three interglacials, and within them, many fluctuations of less intensity.

Period	Epoch	British stages	Upper Thames deposits	Oxygen Isotope Stage	Age in 1000's years	Deep-sea oxygen isotope variation (COLD ← → WARM)
QUATERNARY	HOLOCENE	FLANDRIAN	ALLUVIUM	1		
	PLEISTOCENE — Upper	DEVENSIAN	NORTHMOOR GRAVEL	2, 3, 4		
				a, c, e — 5	100	
		IPSWICHIAN				
	PLEISTOCENE — Middle	WOLSTONIAN	SUMMERTOWN-RADLEY GRAVEL	6		
				7	200	
				8		
			WOLVERCOTE GRAVEL	9	300	
		HOXNIAN	? GLACIAL DEPOSITS	10		
			HANBOROUGH GRAVEL	11	400	
		ANGLIAN		12		
				13	500	
				14		
		CROMERIAN COMPLEX	NORTHERN DRIFT	15	600	
				16 to 21		
	PLEISTOCENE — Lower			?22 to c63	not to scale / 1640	

Ages and climatic environments of Quaternary river deposits in the upper Thames region.
(Based on Table 9, British Regional Geology: London and the Thames Valley, 1996. By permission of the British Geological Survey. © NERC. All rights reserved. IPR/56-33C).

The most severe of the glaciations was the Anglian that took place about 470,000 years ago. The southerly limits of the ice sheet can be mapped from the deposits of boulder clay left behind when the ice melted. Tongues of ice reached Moreton-in-Marsh and Aylesbury, but Oxfordshire was not invaded. The timing and extent of the Wolstonian glaciation in Britain is not clear, but certainly Oxfordshire remained ice-free during this glacial phase. The Devensian brought ice sheets once more to southern Britain, but again Oxfordshire lay a little beyond their southern limit.

Nevertheless, during glacial phases, rocks at the surface,

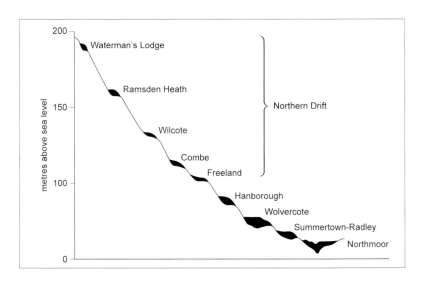

Diagram of the Pleistocene terrace deposits of the upper Thames and Evenlode.

unprotected by vegetation, were shattered by cycles of freezing and thawing, and permanently frozen ground extended to a depth of many metres. At times huge volumes of meltwater swelled the rivers, giving them the power to widen their valleys and also to transport vast quantities of rock waste which were deposited as spreads of sand and gravel across the flood plains. These gravels provide the bulk of the information for unravelling the Quaternary history of the region.

During major cold phases the swollen rivers deepened their valleys, cutting down through gravels of earlier flood plains to leave only remnants of them as terraces on the valley sides. When eventually the bulk of sediment exceeded the power of the river to transport it, the load was deposited as flood plain gravels at the new, lower level. Repetitions of this cycle produce an arrangement of terraces like the steps of a staircase.

The down-cutting power of the rivers resulted from an increase in the gradient of their courses due to a progressive lowering of sea level through the Pleistocene. Superimposed on the overall lowering, which amounts to as much as 150 metres from pre-Pleistocene levels, are lesser rises and falls related to the amount of water accumulating in growing ice sheets or released by their shrinkage.

The oldest surviving deposit of the River Thames is a patch of flinty gravel at Nettlebed, on top of the Chilterns near Henley. It lies about 170 metres above the present course of the river, giving some idea of the vast amount of rock that has been eroded during the Quaternary.

Across Oxfordshire, at least nine other gravel terraces at

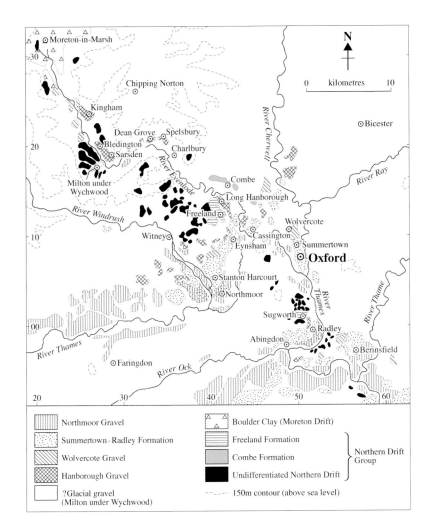

Map labels:

Moreton-in-Marsh
Chipping Norton
Kingham
Dean Grove · Spelsbury
Bledington
Sarsden
Charlbury
Milton under Wychwood
Combe
Long Hanborough
Freeland
Witney
Cassington
Eynsham
Stanton Harcourt
Northmoor
Sugworth
Abingdon
Radley
Faringdon
Berinsfield
Bicester
Wolvercote
Summertown
Oxford

River Cherwell
River Ray
River Evenlode
River Windrush
River Thames
River Thame
River Ock

N

0   kilometres   10

Legend:

- Northmoor Gravel
- Summertown-Radley Formation
- Wolvercote Gravel
- Hanborough Gravel
- ?Glacial gravel (Milton under Wychwood)
- Boulder Clay (Moreton Drift)
- Freeland Formation
- Combe Formation
- Undifferentiated Northern Drift   } Northern Drift Group
- 150m contour (above sea level)

successively lower levels demonstrate the former route of the Thames and its tributaries. They are considered in two groups. Those of the higher, older group are called Plateau Gravels or High Level gravels because they lie outside the modern river valleys. The lower, later deposits are called Valley Gravels.

In the Upper Thames region above the Goring Gap the older group comprises clayey gravel and pebbly clays. This is usually called Northern Drift because the constituent materials are derived from rocks to the north and north-west of Oxfordshire, rather than from the local limestones. The most numerous pebbles and cobbles are a pale brown **quartzite** and white **quartz** originating from Triassic rocks of the West Midlands. These quartzites can be seen in Oxford streets, for example in Merton Street and Radcliffe Square, where they were selected for paving because of their hardness and durability.

The pattern of distribution of the Northern Drift from

Distribution of gravel deposits of the upper Thames region.
(based on Bridgland 1994, Figure 2.1. Reproduced by permission of www. jncc.gov.uk)

above Kingham via Charlbury and Oxford to the Goring Gap indicates the existence of an early Pleistocene river ancestral to the Evenlode and Thames. There is still controversy as to whether this high level river drained a far larger area, including much of the Midlands, than the modern rivers, or whether it merely redistributed material brought into its catchment by glacial action. The highest occurrences of Northern Drift lie at nearly 200 metres above sea level at Leafield and at Waterman's Lodge on the Cornbury Park estate south-west of Charlbury. The train of patches continues south-eastwards at various lower levels by Ramsden Heath, Wilcote, Perrottshill, Cogges Wood and Osney Hill. South of the Thames the Northern Drift is found on Cumnor and Chawley Hursts, across Boars Hill and on the Sinodun Hills. The different levels correspond to periods when the river eroded and redistributed the original material. The two lowest levels are very clearly river terraces. These are the patches of quartzitic gravel at Combe, on the northern side of the Evenlode, lying about 130 metres OD, and the more extensive spread around Freeland, a couple of miles to the south on the other side of the river and some 10 m lower.

High level gravels occur on both sides of the Goring Gap and form extensive spreads across the Chilterns between Goring and Henley. Their main constituent is flint, but the noticeable presence of quartz and quartzite proclaims the link with the Northern Drift. These gravels can be traced below the Goring Gap into the London Basin. Beyond Maidenhead, where the Thames turns south-east, they run north-east towards Watford where they are overlain by deposits of the Anglian glaciation. This early route of the Thames via the Vale of St Albans to southern East Anglia was blocked by the Anglian ice sheet of some 470,000 years ago, forcing the river southwards to more or less its modern course.

One other pre-Anglian deposit of great interest, though no longer visible, is found in a group of channels cut into the Kimmeridge Clay at Sugworth, between Oxford and Abingdon. Discovered during the road works for the A34 Abingdon bypass in 1972-73 in the cutting just south of Bagley Wood, these channels are considered to be meanders of an ancient River Thames which lay 40 metres above the modern river and had a flow probably seven times that of today's river. The sediments that fill the channels are fossiliferous clays, silts, sands and gravels representing an interglacial period half a million years ago. The fossils include beetles, **ostracods,** vertebrates and plant remains. The floral and faunal evidence indicates a temperate climate warmer than today's and the general picture is of a large river flowing through fairly dense mixed oak forest with locally developed clearings and marshy areas of herb-dominated flood plain.

After the Anglian glaciation the Thames and its tributaries became established in their modern-day valleys. Four gravel terraces produced by the continuing process of periodic down-cutting are recognised in the upper Thames valley. The oldest is the Hanborough Gravel terrace, 30 metres above the present river. ('Gravel' refers to the Formation which consists of gravel i.e. pebbles and sand whereas 'terrace' refers to a morphological feature.) Below that is the Wolvercote Gravel terrace, which lies about 16 metres above the present river, followed by the Summertown-Radley Gravel terrace at about 8 metres. Finally comes the Northmoor Gravel terrace at about 3 metres above the present river. The sequence of terraces, like the steps of a staircase, can best be seen at Radley where the college and its playing fields are on the Hanborough Terrace, the church on a patch of Wolvercote Terrace, the station on the Summertown-Radley Terrace and the old village on the Northmoor Terrace. Each gravel is a complex, composite deposit representing thousands of years of river activity and climatic fluctuations. These gravels still contain some brown quartzite derived from the older High Level gravels, but the main bulk of the constituent pebbles are from the rocks within the present valleys.

In the upper Thames, Windrush and Evenlode valleys the gravels are creamy in colour owing to the preponderance of limestone pebbles derived from the Great Oolite. Those of the Cherwell Valley are prevailingly rusty-coloured because of the incorporation of Middle Lias ironstone from the north. By contrast, the gravels of the Thame valley consist almost entirely of flint. Below the confluences of the Cherwell and the Thames the Thames gravels become progressively more mixed in composition and downstream from Dorchester flint begins to predominate over all other constituents.

The Hanborough Gravel Terrace is named from the largest remnant of the deposit on which the villages of Long Hanborough and Church Hanborough are built. Other patches remain across the Oxford Clay country to the south-west, for example, at South Leigh, and between Ducklington and Bampton. Higher up the Evenlode valley the deposits at Dean, near Charlbury were over 4 metres thick and were worked in a number of pits. In the Cherwell valley, the largest patches are those on which Kirtlington and Bletchingdon stand.

It used to be thought that the Hanborough gravel was deposited during a fairly warm phase because it has yielded bones of animals such as **straight-tusked elephant**, horse and red deer. However, recent workers have discovered thin silty beds within the gravel that contain shells of cold-tolerant species of snails characteristic of sub-arctic conditions. Their evidence suggests a treeless, sparsely vegetated landscape during one or more cold phases around 300,000 - 400,000 years ago. The mammal bones are now considered to have become incorporated into the gravel as the river reworked earlier deposits. Reworking probably also accounts for the one man-made flint hand axe recovered from the pits at Long Hanborough.

The Wolvercote gravel terrace is far less extensive than the other terraces and is poorly known. The largest remnant, with a few satellite patches, is at Wolvercote in north Oxford. Apart from that, it is found at Radley – the church is built on it – at two or three points in the lower Evenlode valley near Bladon, and on the west bank of the Cherwell at Shipton between Thrupp and Campsfield.

At Wolvercote in the late 19th century a brick pit revealed an ancient river channel cutting through the terrace gravel and into the underlying Oxford Clay. The channel sediments yielded a number of Lower Palaeolithic flint hand-axes and a variety of fossils, including straight-tusked elephant, **steppe rhinoceros**, ox, horse, reindeer, plants and beetles which indicate deposition under fairly temperate conditions. The hand-axes, 83 in all, are large, extremely well made and fashioned from good quality flint which was presumably imported from the Chilterns. They appear to have been made on the site, possibly by a single craftsman. In spite of their unusual and characteristic form, it is not possible to assign them to a particular age.

The relationship of the channel to the terrace gravel, and their relative ages, is still a matter of debate and will continue to be so until a new exposure yields new data. At present, the original site in the brick pit is covered by the water of the Linkside Lake.

From Wolvercote, the Banbury road into Oxford runs across Oxford Clay as it descends gently about 8 metres to reach Summertown, situated on the northern edge of the gravel terrace on which the city of Oxford is built. This terrace is formed by the gravels of the Summertown-Radley Formation. In the upper Thames Valley extensive deposits of these gravels are preserved from around Fairford all the way to the Goring Gap. The formation has been well exposed in the past in pits at Stanton Harcourt, Cassington, Eynsham, Summertown, Oxford, Radley, Dorchester and other places. The sections differ from place to place, but when pieced together they reveal a complex sequence of different gravels representing accumulation during both temperate and cold conditions between 275,000 and 75,000 years ago.

The gravels that form the bulk of the sequence were laid down in intensely cold, periglacial conditions as is evident at Stanton Harcourt both by structures such as ice wedge casts and shells of cold-climate snails. However, overlying these gravels are deposits which yield interglacial faunas. For example, in the pit at Eynsham, close to the old railway station, remains of hippoptamus were fairly common. This level is dated to about 125,000 years ago.

In recent years, the discovery at Stanton Harcourt of fossiliferous gravels filling an old river channel below the main deposit of 'cold' gravel has demonstrated the existence of an earlier interglacial episode hitherto unrecognised in the British sequence. Dated to about 200,000 years ago these deposits have yielded over 700 bones and teeth of large animals, including mammoth, straight-tusked elephant, horse, bison, lion, bear and hyaena. There are also bones of birds, rodents, frogs and fishes; about 50 species of bivalves and snails; nearly 90 species of insects; and wood, seeds and pollen of oak and hazel. In addition, 27 man-made stone tools have been found.

The lowest, youngest gravel deposit, the Northmoor Gravel, lies more or less at the level of the modern River Thames and its tributaries. It occurs in extensive spreads from below Cirencester all the way into the Goring Gap. Vast quantities of the gravel have been extracted for the needs of modern society, leaving a series of lakes as the worked-out pits have filled with water, as at Ashton Keynes, Fairford, Standlake, Radley, Sutton Courtenay and Dorchester.

Careful study of these gravels reveals a complex history, reflecting the climatic fluctuations of the last 40 or so millennia. At the base, organic-rich sediments yield radiocarbon dates of around 40,000 years. Insect remains are abundant and indicate a climate with cooler summers than

Jaw of bison in gravel of the 200,000 year old channel at Stanton Harcourt. During a glacial episode the growth of an ice wedge cut the bone in two and pushed the pieces apart. When the ice melted the paler sediment sludged in to fill the gap.

A lower molar tooth of a mammoth from Stanton Harcourt. The tooth consists of a series of vertical plates, each like a flattened tube. The wall of the plate is made of enamel – a hard, dense material. The filling inside the walls is dentine, or ivory, which is less hard. The plates are bound together to make a complete tooth by a third kind of bony material called cement which is less hard again. When the tooth is in use the different materials wear down at different rates thus maintaining an efficient rasping and grinding surface.

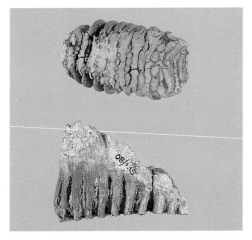

RIGHT Northmoor Gravel at Oday Hill, south of Abingdon. The underlying (blue) rock is Kimmeridge Clay.

BELOW Teeth of baby mammoths from the Stanton Harcourt channel (the teeth are 6 cm long).

BOTTOM Teeth of a lion from the Summertown-Radley gravel in High Street, Oxford.

0   4 cm

today and much colder winters. Plant remains represent a sparse vegetation dominated by grasses and sedges. Bones of large animals include reindeer, red deer, bison, horse and mammoth. The lower part of the gravels accumulated between about 40,000 and 25,000 years ago under arctic conditions. From then on the cold intensified and for the next 12,000 years or so, deposition of sediment more or less ceased while the landscape was frozen solid. At the time of the severest cold, ice sheets estimated to be around 1800 metres thick over Scotland, extended as far south as Cardiff. Oxfordshire, although free of ice, was a barren polar desert. Because of the enormous volumes of water locked up in the ice caps, sea level was as much as 120 metres lower than at present. Britain was joined to the mainland of Europe and the North Sea was mostly a plain.

From about 13,000 to 11,500 years ago the change to a brief temperate interlude is represented in the Northmoor Gravel sequence by bodies of organic-rich sediment with plant and insect remains which overlie the lower part of the gravel. These are overlain by another metre or so of gravel that was laid down by the renewal of cold conditions, when glaciers once again returned to the British highlands. Finally, about 10,000 years ago, the present mild period began and gravel deposition ceased.

RIVER GRAVELS OF SOUTH-EAST OXFORDSHIRE

On the Chiltern slope within the loop of the Thames between Goring and Henley numerous patches of quartzite-bearing plateau gravels at different levels record the passage of the early Pleistocene river, while extensive deposits of later gravels lie within the confines of the modern valley. All these gravels present a contrast with those of the Upper Thames above the Goring Gap in being principally composed of pebbles of flint. Although these various gravels are given local names to identify them, they can be correlated with equivalents in the upper Thames, principally on the basis of heights above the present river.

OTHER PLEISTOCENE DEPOSITS

The ridges of the Chilterns are extensively capped by a deposit called Clay-with-flints. As the name suggests, it consists generally of a brown, sandy clay containing broken, angular flint, flint nodules and blocks of sarsen. In places it is so clayey that it has been dug for bricks, while elsewhere, flint predominates and was worked for gravel. Resting on an uneven, deeply eroded surface of Chalk, it varies rapidly in thickness from place to place. The maximum recorded depth is over 6 metres. It is thought to have originated as the residue of Chalk and Tertiary strata, partly resulting from the dissolution of the Chalk by rainwater and partly by glacial and periglacial weathering of those strata. The distribution of Clay-with-flints in southern England suggest that it once blanketed the entire Chalk surface before erosion dissected it into the patches that remain today. Thus on the Downs of Oxfordshire, Clay-with-flints is less widely preserved than on the Chilterns. This accounts for the difference in character of the two ranges, because the deeper clay supports the growth of trees better than the thin soils of the Chalk.

HEAD AND COOMBE DEPOSITS

During periglacial periods in Oxfordshire the erosion of rocks was accelerated by alternations of freezing and thawing. In spring, when the snows melted, the frost-shattered rock debris formed a slurry which gradually flowed down slopes over the frozen subsoil. This material, generally known as Head, is widely distributed across the county in valley bottoms and at the foot of slopes, chiefly in the Chalk country. Head generally consists of an unstratified jumble of clay, clayey sand, flints and other local rock fragments. The characteristic variety in the dry valleys of the Chalk country – an amorphous mass of Chalk fragments, with or without flint – is called Coombe Rock. It forms the valley floors around Fingest and Turville and from Stonor down to Henley.

Flows of Head, from Anglian times onward, account for the fans of chalky, flinty gravel at the foot of the steep coombes of the Chiltern escarpment, often called the Wallingford Fan gravels. They coalesced to form probably a continuous sheet of gravel sloping to the north-west. Much has since been eroded and incorporated into later river gravels, but extensive patches remain stretching from near Goring in the south, north via Ipsden and Ewelme to Cuxham and Brightwell Baldwin. In the Chinnor district remnants of these gravels cap low ridges between the tributary streams of the River Thame. At a number of places near Turners Court and around Ewelme, working pits have yielded many fine flint implements representing several different periods of human occupation.

HOLOCENE EPOCH

About 10,000 years ago the climatic conditions improved and the Holocene Epoch, the warm period in which we are now living, began. In the gentler weather the rivers no longer became the mighty floods of periglacial times. Their power and size were diminished so that their shrunken descendants now lie in oversized valleys. No longer able to move gravel, at first they lined their channels with mud, but as the forests developed, covering Oxfordshire and stabilising the soil, so even mud became in short supply.

This stability was not altered by the activities of Mesolithic hunter-gatherer people nor by the small scale farming of their Neolithic successors. In contrast, from about 2000 years ago in the late Iron Age, and intensifying greatly in the Roman period, arable cultivation exposed soils to erosion on a large scale, mainly on Cotswold slopes. The rivers thus acquired a sediment load that at times of flooding was redeposited over the valley floors. This deposit is the alluvium that forms the modern flood plains. It is a dark, silty clay, often 2 or 3 metres thick near the river, thinning towards the outer edge.

Extensive arable farming and the consequent deposition of alluvium declined rapidly after the end of the Roman period and the collapse of the villa system. However, a second period of alluviation took place, coinciding with the revival of

Divisions of Holocene time.

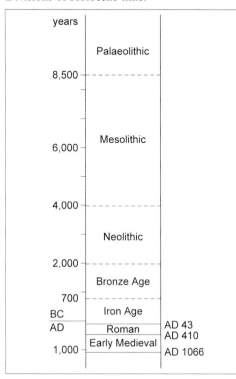

agriculture that began in mid-Saxon times and intensified steadily up to the Black Death in the 14th century. Thereafter extensive arable farming, contributing to soil erosion, began again only in the 20th century. Today the Thames carries about 200,000 tonnes of sediment to the sea each year, but flood control along its length ensures that little of this load is left on the flood plains.

The Chiltern escarpment at Beacon Hill, near Aston Rowant. The chalk formations forming the steep slope originally extended beyond the horizon to the north (left). Erosion during Tertiary and Quaternary time has uncovered the older beds of the country below and created this escarpment.

ELEVEN

THE ARRIVAL OF MAN

The earliest man-like species are known from fossils in Africa over 2 million years old. In Britain the oldest remains are the shin bone and two teeth from Boxgrove in Sussex, dated to about half a million years ago, and the famous skull from Swanscombe in Kent, which is about 400,000 years old. In Oxfordshire the earliest evidence for ancient people is represented by the single flint hand axe recovered from the Hanborough gravels, again about 400,000 years old.

An immense length of time, some 100,000 years, separates this find from the collection of 83 stone tools in the Wolvercote Channel. The fresh condition and sharp edges of these artefacts suggests that they were made very near by. Some are made of quartzite, which was abundantly available in the local gravels, but most are of high quality flint which must have been carried in by hand, presumably from the Chilterns, around 20 km away.

The gravels of the Summertown-Radley Formation have yielded numerous flint tools, indicating that over many thousands of years hunter/gatherer people visited this remote corner of Europe during milder periods.

There is no evidence of human activity in Britain from about 120,000 to 60,000 years ago. Perhaps the preceding cold period had driven people far to the south and their return was blocked by the rise in sea level that followed.

Between 60,000 and 25,000 years ago, the climate oscillated between warmer and cooler episodes and sea levels fell again by 50 to 80 metres below those of today. Neanderthal people lived in England during favourable periods but, as yet, evidence of their occupation in Oxfordshire amounts to little more than one or two typical flint hand axes from around Abingdon. By about 31,000 years ago modern man had arrived in Britain, but no traces of these people are known from Oxfordshire.

During the severely cold period from 25,000 to 13,000 years ago, populations of modern man seem to have retreated to southern parts of Europe. From 13,000 years ago a period of rapid warming re-established a milder climate that lasted a millenium and a half. Cold conditions prevailed once again from about 11,000 to 10,000 years ago, followed by the rapid warming which signalled the start of the Holocene, the warm phase in which we live today.

The first people to return were the final representatives of the Palaeolithic or old Stone Age. Their flint tools have been found at a site dated to the earliest Holocene at Gatehampton, near Goring. Other isolated specimens are found across the county. The story of subsequent populations of Mesolithic hunter/gatherers, Neolithic farmers and their Bronze Age and Iron Age successors is the province of archaeology.

But the geological story is not finished. The earth is not static. The continual movement of the continents, the dramatic power of volcanoes and earthquakes and the slow but inexorable work of frost and rain, rivers and tides are active agents of geological change, even though they hardly affect Oxfordshire in the course of a human lifetime.

Man himself has become a geological agent. People are now so numerous and widespread that their needs for living space, farm land and materials have affected almost every part of the land surface and have already pushed many species of animals and plants into extinction. Intensive agriculture and clearing of forests threaten to increase erosion and flooding, and to perturb local climates.

Far more serious is the threat of global warming driven by ever increasing emissions of carbon dioxide and other greenhouse gases into the atmosphere from cars, aeroplanes, power stations and so on. The main risks are increased melting of polar ice with consequent rises in sea level, disruption of oceanic and atmospheric circulation, and altered regional climates. In Oxfordshire alone, each person, on average, is contributing carbon dioxide to the atmosphere at a rate of 9.25 tons per year. This is more than twice the world average and ten times that of a person in Bangladesh.

Flint tools from (left to right) Long Hanborough, Wolvercote, and Summertown.

TWELVE

TIME AND MOTION

In this short geological account of Oxfordshire the changes of physical geography between sea and land that took place over millions of years have been described as the result of global or local movements of the earth's crust. Although the crust seems massively solid and stable, at least to us in Oxfordshire, where earthquakes are rare, it is, in fact, only a thin skin floating on the hot and mobile interior. In relative terms, the crust is about as thick as a layer of paper pasted onto a football. It is made up of a number of slabs or plates of rock which are ever on the move.

The floors of the oceans are formed from plates of denser rock, 5-10 kilometres thick. In contrast, plates that carry continents are usually about 35 kilometres thick and composed of less dense material. New rock is added to an oceanic plate along mid-ocean fissures where molten material wells up from below to form vast submarine mountain chains - the longest, linear features on the earth's surface. This upwelling pushes the two halves of the plate apart and forces them against neighbouring plates. When two oceanic plates are forced against each other, one plate normally slides underneath the other. As the descending plate sinks deeper, it melts and produces material to power volcanoes far above at the surface.

In contrast, when two continental plates collide, or a continental plate is pushed up against an oceanic plate, the lighter rocks, instead of sinking, are crumpled up to form mountain chains. The great compressive and tensional forces caused by these powerful earth movements also cause faulting, or fracturing of rocks, along which vertical or horizontal movement takes place.

Thus, oceans open and close, mountains ranges arise, and are worn down again by erosion, the land rises and falls, seas come and go; the earth is never still. The rate at which earth movements operate is imperceptibly slow by the measure of a human lifetime, but over immense periods of time the results are dramatic. For example, sixty million or so years ago the

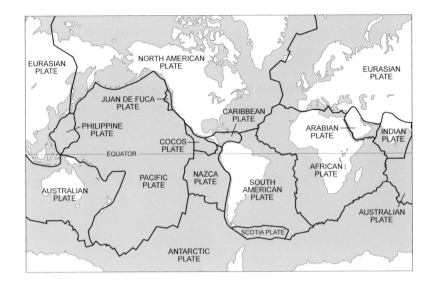

site that is now Oxford was buried under a blanket of sedimentary rocks over 400 metres thick which is now gone, eroded away at an average rate of erosion of just one millimetre per hundred and fifty years.

Examples such as this clearly demonstrate the fundamental importance of time in geological processes. In order to understand geological history it is useful to know how time is measured and ordered. Geological time can be considered in two different ways. On one hand there is relative time, which orders events in relation each other. On the other, there is absolute time, which places events within a numerical scale of years.

Absolute time can be calculated by means of radiochemical dating. This makes use of the principle that radioactive chemical elements change spontaneously into more stable daughter elements. For example, uranium-238, that is, uranium composed of atoms that each weigh 238 atomic units, slowly changes into lead-206. The rate of change, expressed as the half-life, or the time taken for 50% of the original element to have changed, is constant and can be measured. When the half-life is known and the proportions of parent and daughter element are measured, it is possible to calculate how much time has elapsed since radioactive decay began. Different elements are used to date different types of geological material.

For example, uranium–238 is a commonly used to date igneous rocks, that is rocks which formed by crystallising from a molten state. As soon as solid minerals have crystallised the radioactive minerals within begin their transmutation. The 4,510 million year half-life of uranium–238 enables very ancient rocks to be dated. In contrast, carbon–14, with a half-life of 5,730 years, is useful for dating materials such as bone or charcoal aged between 200 years and 50,000 years.

Radiochemical dating is not generally applicable to sedimentary rocks, which are formed by the accumulation of particles of a variety of pre-existing rocks (although where an igneous rock occurs within a sedimentary sequence it can be used to give an indication of the age of the beds immediately above and below it). Instead, sedimentary rocks are placed in order by relative dating, based on the science of stratigraphy.

This relies on the simple principle that in a sequence, or pile, of sedimentary rocks a particular bed is younger than the one below it and older than the one above it, provided it has not been overturned by earth movements. The assemblage of fossils in each bed acts as a label which enables that bed to be correlated with one of the same age at a more distant location.

The most useful fossils for dating rocks over large areas are those of animals that had wide distributions – for example, animals that swam freely in the seas – and which evolved rapidly, so that different forms are found from one bed to the next. In Jurassic and Cretaceous strata the best fossils for the purpose are ammonites. These organisms, related to modern squids and octopuses, are represented by their shells, usually coiled in the form of a flat spiral. In the Lower Jurassic, for example, ammonites can be used to identify twenty different levels.

In this way local successions can be built up to regional successions and eventually to worldwide schemes of classification. On this basis geological time is divided into units called Eras and Periods, similar in concept to familiar historical terms such as Bronze Age or Tudor Period. Geological Periods are represented by rock units called Formations which are named after a characteristic type of rock or from a typical place of occurrence, for example, the White Limestone, or, the Oxford Clay. For more detailed studies, rock units can be subdivided into smaller and smaller units using a similar method.

THIRTEEN

GEOLOGY FROM THE TRAIN

Between Reading and Moreton-in-Marsh the railway from London to Hereford passes successively across the Cretaceous and Jurassic strata from youngest to oldest. These notes briefly describe some of the geological features that can be seen from the train.

READING TO PANGBOURNE

This stretch lies in the lower, more open part of the Goring Gap. On the right, the steep, wooded slopes of the Chiltern Hills are of Upper Chalk, thickly spread with gravels laid down by the Thames at various times during the Pleistocene.

PANGBOURNE TO GORING

Just beyond Pangbourne station, on the right, the wall of the cutting is a vertical face of pure white Upper Chalk with thin bands of black flints. The line continues in a cutting through the Upper Chalk for almost 2 kilometres emerging at Basildon within the narrowest section of the gorge. Between Basildon and Goring the route lies on river gravels which slope gently down towards the concave bends of the river.

GORING TO CHOLSEY

From Goring the line soon enters a cutting where the pale rock glimpsed through the vegetation is the Middle Chalk. After the river is crossed again, the next cutting, slightly less overgrown, shows grey Lower Chalk.

CHOLSEY TO DIDCOT

Cholsey church, standing alone in the fields on the right just beyond the station, is a conspicuous landmark on the bare slopes of Cholsey Hill. This hill, carved mainly out of Lower Chalk, is the core of a former loop of the Thames.

With the Goring Gap now behind the views open out. To the left is the Chalk scarp of the Downs. To the right the scarp continues as the distant line of the Chiltern Hills. Nearer, the two prominent tree-crowned hills are the Wittenham Clumps. They form the western end of the Sinodun Hills, a miniature range formed from Upper

Greensand capped with Lower Chalk and patches of ancient river gravel.

From South Moreton the line runs for a kilometre and a half through a shallow cutting in the Upper Greensand, visible here and there under the vegetation, as a pale rock resembling grey Lower Chalk.

Beyond the cutting the line to Didcot runs over flat country underlain by Gault Clay.

DIDCOT TO OXFORD

Didcot station stands on the eastern end of the belt of ' head' that forms an apron along the foot of the Downs. Head is an unstratified deposit formed during the Pleistocene 'ice age' when repeated cycles of freeze and thaw turned frost-shattered rock into a slurry that flowed down steep north-facing slopes.

A kilometre or so north of Didcot, the Gault Clay is covered by late Pleistocene river gravels. Worked out gravel pits, now filled with water, can be seen on the left. The river is then crossed again, and shortly after Culham station the line passes through a short cutting in the spur of Lower Greensand on which the park of Nuneham Courtenay stands. The Greensand forms the steep wooded bluff above the river, seen on the right as the train comes out of the cutting and crosses the river again.

On both sides, approaching Radley, flooded pits show where late Pleistocene river gravels have been extracted. After Radley, the line runs along the upper edge of a gravel deposit of the Summertown-Radley formation. On the right, the gravel makes the level ground, occupying a terrace cut into the Kimmeridge Clay. On the left the clay itself forms the rising ground.

At Kennington, the streets of houses (on the left) are built on the sands and limestones of the Corallian Formation while the wooded hillside above is Kimmeridge Clay. Higher ground closes in on the right as the line passes through the 'Sandford Gap', a humble equivalent of the Goring Gap, where the river has breached the Corallian scarp.

The line passes under the southern bypass road and approaches Oxford across the Thames alluvium. On the left, Boars Hill and Hinksey Hill are part of the Oxford to Faringdon ridge of Corallian rocks. Here the Corallian sands and limestones are sandwiched between a base of Oxford Clay and a cap of Kimmeridge Clay.

A kilometre or so north of Oxford station, on the left, there is a good view over Port Meadow, a great level expanse of the Thames flood plain covered with alluvium through which a few 'islands' of gravel protrude. Beyond are the hills of Wytham and Seacourt; outlying masses of the Oxford to Faringdon Corallian ridge, capped with Coral Rag limestone.

The line passes under two road bridges and then runs alongside a series of pits from which late Pleistocene Northmoor gravels are being, or have been, extracted. In 1994, in the Oxford Clay underlying the pits, the skeleton of a 5 metre-long pliosaur was discovered. The specimen is now on display at the Oxford University Museum. The Oxford Clay forms the floor of the low-lying Thames valley stretching into the distance. The spire of Cassington church is a conspicuous feature.

The line crosses the River Evenlode and over a road as it approaches Hanborough Station. On the right, just before the station, the buildings of the industrial site occupy the old Hanborough Station Quarry. The stone produced here, a coarse, shelly, oolitic limestone came from the Middle Jurassic Forest Marble Formation. The quarry was active during the first half of the twentieth century. In the post war 1940s, for example, it supplied the walling stone for Oxford University's new Geology Department and for the Botany and Forestry schools.

HANBOROUGH TO CHARLBURY

This 10 kilometre section of the route lies in the Evenlode Gorge. In the first half of this stretch the valley consists of the meanders of an older and much more powerful river which cut deeply into the Great Oolite limestone. The concave sides of its bends are marked by cusps, or spurs of land – five pointing right (north), five to the left (south). Each spur points into a steep high bank, like an amphitheatre, usually wooded, formed by the undercutting of the former river on the convex side of its loops. The present river is too small to have cut this deep gorge and is termed a misfit.

The line crosses six of the spurs by embankments and shallow cuttings in which the limestones can be glimpsed, then enters the upper, straight part of the gorge. The walls of the valley from here on comprise a range of Middle and Lower Jurassic strata from the Great Oolite limestones down to clays of the Lias.

At the hamlet of Fawler, on the right, the former brick field in the Upper Lias lay close to the line. Beyond the houses, pits were opened in the 1860s to dig the Middle Lias Marlstone for iron ore. Production of this so-called Bleinheim Iron Ore ceased in 1885.

From Charlbury the valley begins to widen and the slopes are less steep. From Shipton-under-Wychwood the line swings northwards and the hill slopes of Middle Jurassic rocks recede, forming a large bowl with a floor of Lower Lias clay. The line runs beside the river through hummocky terrain formed by patches of river gravels laid down at various times in the Middle and later Pleistocene. The sides of the bowl curve back towards the river, leaving a low gap between Adlestrop and Oddington. Beyond the gap the Vale of Moreton opens out. To the left, the Cotswold scarp, largely comprising Middle Jurassic limestones, curves in a semicircle around Moreton-in-Marsh. The Lower Lias clay floor of the Vale is extensively spread with a range of Pleistocene sands, gravels and clays carved into a low hilly landscape by small streams. The deposits represent glacial outwash streams, ice-dammed lakes and moraines of an Anglian ice sheet active between about 450,000 and 350,000 years ago.

GLOSSARY

Aerobic: describes conditions where oxygen is freely available.

Anaerobic: describes conditions where free oxygen is absent.

Alluvium: the silty clay that forms the floor of the river valleys. It is formed from soil erosion and was deposited mainly from the late Iron Age (a little over 2,000 years ago) and in the Roman Period.

Ammonites: an extinct group of molluscs related to squids and octopuses. The shell is usually coiled in a flat spiral and is divided internally into chambers like that of the living pearly nautilus.

Aragonite: a form of calcium carbonate. It differs from the more stable and more abundant form, calcite, in its crystal structure. It is an important constituent of the shells of many molluscs.

Ashlar: squared blocks of stone used in level courses for the facing of walls.

Belemnites: an extinct group of cephalopod molluscs related to modern squids and cuttlefish. The squid-like body had an internal skeleton consisting mainly of a hard, calcareous bullet-shaped feature. This is the part that is usually found as a fossil.

Bivalves: a group of widespread and abundant molluscs. The body is protected by two shells or valves that mirror each other. Typical examples are cockles, mussels and oysters.

Boulder Clay: an unstratified and unsorted mixture of clay, sand, gravel and boulders collected by, and laid down beneath, a glacier or ice sheet.

Brachiopods: a group of marine animals with paired shells. Sometimes confused with bivalves but in brachiopods the two shells are unequal in size and are bilaterally symmetrical. The body plan is different also.

Bryozoans: aquatic, invertebrate animals living as colonies. Each individual is a tiny tube with a ring of tentacles around the mouth. It secretes a skeleton of calcium carbonate and the colony as a whole may encrust solid surfaces or grow in a branching, tree-like form.

Calcareous: made of, or containing, calcium carbonate.

Calcite: the common, crystalline form of calcium carbonate. It is the principal mineral component of limestones and forms the hard parts of many invertebrate animals, for example, oysters and sea urchins.

Carbon dating: a 'normal' carbon atom has an atomic weight of 12, notated C-12. Carbon atoms with an atomic weight of 14 are created in the atmosphere by the action of cosmic rays on nitrogen. This C-14 is radioactive and reverts to nitrogen at a known rate. All organisms take in both forms of carbon but when they die the C-14 slowly reverts to nitrogen. The relative proportions of the two forms in tissue such as bone or wood can thus be used to calculate the time that has elapsed since the death of the organism.

The rate of change of C-14 back to nitrogen is expressed as the half-life. About half the C-14 reverts in about 5,730 years. This short half-life means that the C-14 dating method is useful only for relatively recent materials up to about 40,000 years old.

Concretion: a mass of hardened sediment, generally rounded, which formed during or after the deposition of the host sediment by localised deposition of cementing material, such as calcite, from solution.

Coprolite: the fossilised faeces of fishes, reptiles, birds and mammals, generally in the form of rounded, black stones rich in calcium phosphate. The term was extended in the mid-nineteenth century to the blackened, phosphatised fossils that form deposits thick enough to be worth extracting to make fertiliser.

Cross-bedding: a series of bedding planes inclined to the main planes of stratification of the strata, usually indicating deposition by current-action. See, for example, the picture of the sands at Tubney Wood on page 47.

Dogger: boulder-sized, spherical, calcareous concretion within unconsolidated sediment. The term nodule is used for smaller concretions.

Dressings: building stones specially shaped for plinths, corners, door frames, chimneys and so on.

Epoch: see Period.

Era: see Period.

Facies: the sum of the characteristics of a sedimentary rock, such as, lithology, bedding-style and fossils, which reflect the environmental conditions at the time of deposition.

Fault: a fracture surface along which rock masses have moved relative to each other, vertically, laterally or horizontally.

Ferruginous: rich in iron compounds.

Freestone: a building stone whose properties are more or less equal in all directions, so that it is especially suitable for dressings and for carving.

Glauconite: a green mineral rich in iron and potassium. The conditions under which it forms are not fully understood but in the world today it is found on many continental shelves at depths from a few tens of metres to a few hundreds of metres, generally in areas with low rates of sedimentation.

Greenhouse Gases: energy from the sun comes to earth as short-wave radiation. The earth radiates it back as long-wave radiation. Greenhouse gases, such as carbon dioxide, methane and water vapour, trap a proportion of the long-wave radiation (as does the glass in a greenhouse) thereby warming the atmosphere.

Ichthyosaurs: extinct marine reptiles similar in form to modern dolphins.

Lias: derived from old French liois, meaning compact limestone. It is used geologically to mean the Lower Jurassic Period and its rocks.

London Platform: part of a fairly stable region, stretching from the London area to the Ardennes, that remained relatively high through the Jurassic and Cretaceous Periods. Sometimes just above sea level, sometimes just below. Its influence on the Oxford area, situated in the shallows at its western end, resulted in relatively thin and discontinuous rock sequences.

Marl: a calcareous clay.

Marcasite: a sulphide of iron, like pyrite, but with a different crystal form and less common.

Molluscs: a group of invertebrate animals that includes gastropods (snails), bivalves, belemnites and ammonites.

Mudstone: a fine-grained unlaminated rock composed of particles of clay or clay and silt.

Neanderthal Man: people of a species distinct from modern Man, who lived in Europe and western Asia from about 230,000 to 30,000 years ago.

Ostracods: a group of crustaceans. The animals are mostly less than 1 millimetre long and the body is enclosed in a bivalved carapace. They inhabit a range of aquatic environments and as fossils they are useful as indicators of the freshwater, brackish or marine origins of sediments.

Oxygen Isotopes: Isotopes are varieties of a chemical element whose atoms have a common number of protons but differ in the number of neutrons. They have the same chemical properties but different atomic weights. Most elements consist of a mixture of isotopes.

Isotopes of oxygen in fossils can be used to estimate the temperature of the sea in which the animal lived. When the sea is warmer and evaporation increases the water molecules that pass more readily to the atmosphere are those containing the lighter isotope, O-16. This results in a corresponding increase in the heavier isotope, O-18, in the water. The oxygen incorporated into the shells of marine animals as carbonate reflects the contemporary ratio of its isotopes which then provide a measure of temperature.

Period: a major, worldwide, standard unit of geological time defined by characteristic rock formations and fossils. When used formally the term has a capital letter, e.g., Jurassic Period. A period may be divided into epochs, e.g., the Pleistocene Epoch of the Quaternary Period. A number of periods are grouped together as an era, e.g., the Triassic, Jurassic and Cretaceous Periods comprise the Mesozoic Era.

Pleistocene Epoch: The beginning of the Pleistocene is taken by many geologists in north-west Europe as 2.4 million years ago when there is evidence of a first major cold period from pollen records in land sediments. The formal definition, however, puts the beginning at 1.8 million years ago. This is based on the marine sequence of southern Italy at the level where the faunas record major cooling.

Plesiosaurs: an extinct group of marine reptiles. They had a barrel-shaped body with a rather short tail and limbs modified into paddles or fins. Some types had a long neck and small head while others, generally known as pliosaurs, had a short neck and large head.

Pterosaurs: an extinct group of flying reptiles, contemporaries of the dinosaurs and distantly related to them. The wing consisted of a membrane supported by the bones of a greatly elongated fourth finger.

Pyrite: a widespread form of iron sulphide, FeS_2. It commonly occurs in fine-grained sedimentary rocks and indicates anaerobic conditions. It is also known as Fools Gold on account of its brassy lustre.

Quartz: silica or silicon dioxide, SiO_2, an extremely abundant mineral. It is the major constituent of most sands.

Quartzite: a dense, tough rock made up of grains of quartz sand which have been further cemented together by more quartz deposited from solution or by grains fusing together under pressure along shared grain boundaries.

Rock: any mass of mineral matter, whether consolidated or not, that forms part of the earth's crust. Clay and loose sand are rocks just as much as limestone or granite.

Sauropod: a group of dinosaurs typified by the well known 'brontosaurus'. Typically they had a small head on a long neck, a short, heavy body, legs like an elephant's and a long tail. They were all herbivorous and include the largest known land animals.

Sedimentary Rock: one formed from particles of rock or grains of minerals ranging from mud through silt and sand to gravel and cobbles.

Siliceous: containing silica, SiO_2, a compound of silicon and oxygen which are the two commonest elements of the earth's crust.

Stonesfield Slate: This is the formal name for these beds. The stone is a grey, calcareous sandstone with abundant, tiny flakes of mica, and streaks and patches of white ooliths (see chapter 4). It is not a slate in the geological sense of the word but rather a tilestone. True slate is a fine-grained rock formed from mud by heat and pressure in the earth's crust. The pressure causes the minerals to realign so that the rock develops planes of cleavage in a direction unrelated to the original bedding.

Spicules: tiny siliceous or calcareous objects, commonly needle-shaped or branched, contained within the tissues of sponges to stiffen them.

SSSI: Site of Special Scientific Interest

Steppe Rhinoceros: (*Dicerorhinus hemitoechus*) also called the narrow-nosed rhinoceros. An extinct species of rhinoceros adapted to temperate climatic conditions. It carried its head in a hanging posture like the present-day white rhino. Its teeth were high-crowned to cope with the abrasive grasses of the steppe.

   In cold periods the rhinoceroses were represented by a different species, the woolly rhino (*Coelodonta antiquitatis*).

Straight-tusked Elephant: (*Palaeoloxodon antiquus*) a species of elephant that appeared in Europe about 500,000 years ago and became extinct about 50,000 years ago. It was a large animal, measuring about 4 metres high at the shoulder. Adapted to temperate conditions it lived in grassy plains and lightly wooded habitats. Occasionally it co-existed with the Woolly Mammoth, as at Stanton Harcourt. (see page 83). The mammoth had curving tusks and was adapted for living in colder conditions.

Theropods: a group of dinosaurs that includes all the known bipedal, carnivorous forms. The general appearance is typified by the well known *Tyrannosaurus*.

FURTHER INFORMATION

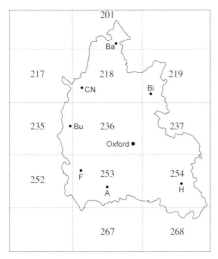

Index sheet of geological maps covering Oxfordshire.

A   Abingdon
Ba   Banbury
Bi   Bicester
Bu   Burford
CN Chipping Norton
F   Faringdon
H   Henley

Oxfordshire is fully covered by the Geological maps published by the British Geological Survey mostly at a scale of 1:50,000. They can be obtained from the British Geological Survey, Sales Desk, Keyworth, Nottingham, NG12 5GG. Website: www.bgs.ac.uk

An accompanying explanatory Memoir for each map is available, except where noted.

Sheet 201 Banbury
    217 Moreton-in-Marsh
    218 Chipping Norton (1 inch to the mile)
    219 Buckingham (with brief explanatory booklet)
    235 Cirencester
    236 Witney
    237 Thame
    252 Swindon (no Memoir)
    253 Abingdon (1 inch to the mile. No Memoir)
    254 Henley-on-Thames
    267 Hungerford (1 inch to the mile)
    268 Reading (with brief explanatory booklet)

MEMOIRS OF THE GEOLOGICAL SURVEY:
Sheet 201. Edmonds, E.A., E.G.Poole and V.Wilson, 1965. Geology of the Country around Banbury and Edge Hill.
Sheet 217. Richardson, L., 1929. The Country around Moreton-in-Marsh.
Sheet 218. Horton, A., E.G.Poole, B.J.Williams, V.C.Illing, G.D.Hobson, 1987. Geology of the Country around Chipping Norton.
Sheet 219 Sumbler, M., 2002. Geology of the Buckingham District (a brief explanation of the geological map).
Sheet 235 Richardson, L., 1933. The Country around Cirencester.
Sheet 236 Richardson, L., W.J.Arkell, and H.G.Dines, 1946. Geology of the Country around Witney.
Sheet 237 Horton, A., M.G.Sumbler, B.M.Cox, K.Ambrose., 1995. Geology of the Country around Thame.
Sheet 254 Jukes-Browne, A.J. and H.J.Osborne White, 1908. Geology of the Country around Henley-on-Thames and Wallingford.
Sheet 267 White, H.J.O., 1907. Geology of the Country around Hungerford and Newbury.
Sheet 268 Mathers, S.J. and N.J.P.Smith, 2000. Geology of the Reading District (a brief explanation of the geological map).

GENERAL:

Arkell, W. J., *The Geology of Oxford*, 1947. Clarendon Press, Oxford.
  Oxford Stone, 1947. Faber.
  'The Building-stones of Blenheim Palace, Cornbury Park, Glympton
  Park and Heythrop House, Oxfordshire', 1948. *Oxoniensia*, XIII,
  49-54.
Aston, M. A., *Stonesfield Slate*, 1974. Oxfordshire County Council,
  Department of Museum Services Publication No.5.
Bond, S .J., S. Gosling & J. Rhodes, *The Clay Industries of
  Oxfordshire*. Oxfordshire Brickmakers, 1980. Oxfordshire
  Museums Service Publication number 14. ISBN 0 901036 07 2.
Bridgland, D. R., *Quaternary of the Thames*, 1994. Geological
  Conservation Review Series: Joint Nature Conservation Committee.
  Chapman & Hall, London. ISBN 0 412 48830 2.
Cope, J. C. W., J. K. Ingham & P. F. Rawson, (Editors), *Atlas of
  Palaeogeography*, 1992. Geological Society of London Memoir no.
  13. ISBN 0-903317-65-6. (The geography of Britain from 850
  million years ago).
Cox, B. M. & M .G. Sumbler, *British Middle Jurassic Stratigraphy*,
  2002. Geological Conservation Review Series: Joint Nature
  Conservation Committee, Peterborough. ISBN 1 86107 479 4. (Has
  details of quarries including Horsehay, Charlbury, Stonesfield, Hook
  Norton).
Edmonds, E., *The Geological Map: an anatomy of the landscape*,
  1983. British Geological Survey. ISBN 0 11 880721 8.
Galton, P. M. & H. P. Powell, *Camptosaurus prestwichii*, 1980.
  Palaeontology vol.23, pp 411-443. (The dinosaur from Cumnor).
Martill, D. M. & J. D. Hudson, *Fossils of the Oxford Clay*, 1991. The
  Palaeontological Association. ISBN 0-901702-46-3.
Morton, J. L., *Strata: How William Smith drew the First Map of the
  Earth in 1801 and Inspired the Science of Geology*, 2001. Tempus
  Publishing Ltd, Stroud. ISBN 0 7524 1992 7.
Natural History Museum, London, *British Mesozoic Fossils*, 2001
  (sixth edition). ISBN 1-898298-73-4. (Illustrations of many of the
  commoner fossils of the Jurassic and Cretaceous).
Smith, A. B. & D. J. Batten, (Editors), *Fossils of the Chalk*, 2002
  (second edition). The Palaeontological Association.
  ISBN 0 901702 78 1.
Sumbler, M. G. (Compiler),. *British Regional Geology. London and the
  Thames Valley*, 1996. 4th Edition. HMSO. ISBN 0 11 884522 5.
Winchester, S., *The Map that changed the World: the tale of William
  Smith and the birth of a science*, 2001. Viking. ISBN 0-670-88407-3.
Wright. J. K. & B. M. Cox, *British Upper Jurassic Stratigraphy*, 2001.
  Geological Conservation Review Series No. 21, Joint Nature
  Conservation Committee, Peterborough. ISBN 1 86107 782 4.

The Oxford University Museum of Natural History has extensive
displays on rocks, fossils and minerals as well as a gallery devoted to
the geology of Oxfordshire. The Museum's address: Parks Road,
Oxford, OX1 3PW. Tel: 01865 272950. Web site: www.oum.ox.ac.uk

ACKNOWLEDGEMENTS

I am grateful to friends who kindly read the manuscript and offered helpful comments; Paul Clasby, David Fielding, Jim Kennedy, Nina Morgan, Tim Palmer and Jon Radley. I especially thank Nina Morgan for producing a typescript from my manuscript in pencilled longhand.

I also thank David Sansom for draughting the maps and diagrams and Rennison Hall for photographic help.

The following organisations have kindly allowed me to make use of illustrations for which they own the copyright:

The Geologists' Association. The geological map on page 11 is based on Figure 1 in G.A. Guide no. 3, *The Oxford District*, by W.S. McKerrow and W.J. Kennedy.

The Natural History Museum, London. The William Smith map of Oxfordshire on page 31.

The British Geological Survey. The Ages of Quaternary river deposits in the upper Thames on page 77 is based on Table 9 in British Regional Geology: London and the Thames Valley, 1996.

Joint Nature Conservation Committee. The map of the upper Thames gravel deposits on page 79 is based on Bridgland 1994. figure 2.1.

Oxford University Museum of Natural History. Restoration of dinosaurs by Gareth Monger on pages 34 (*Megalosaurus*), 36 (*Cetiosaurus*) and 51 (*Camptosaurus prestwichii*).

Julian Comrie kindly provided the front cover photograph of the view from Beacon Hill, Wittenham Clumps on pages 2/3, the Ironstone countryside near Hornton on page 10, the monument to William Smith on page 30 and Beacon Hill and the Chiltern escarpment on page 87.

Jim Kennedy provided the photograph of the Stonesfield slate mine on page 34 and Kate Scott that of the bison jaw on page 83.

I should also like to record my indebtedness to my old friend and mentor James M. Edmonds, Curator of the Geological Collections at the Oxford University Museum of Natural History, 1955-1976, from whom I learned a great deal beside the Geology of Oxfordshire.

Finally, I acknowledge the work of many geologists, professional and amateur, past and present, on which this book is based.

INDEX